A TREASURY of BEST-LOVED HYMNS

WITH·THEIR·STORIES·TOLD
by·DANIEL·A·POLING
&·WITH·DESIGNS·BY
JAMES·H·DAUGHERTY
PICKWICK·PRESS

Foreword

MUSIC not only soothes the savage heart, but has a ministry for every mood and circumstance of the human soul. In its simplest forms and with its most primitive instruments, as with the classics of the ages, it makes articulate the voice of the spirit. Here, without prejudice to any other volume, are the favorites of the American people—the old and the new, the simple and the great. The illustrations from the inspired imagination of James Daugherty have added a richness to the stories and made luminous their divine emotion. From "Holy, Holy, Holy," named by Alfred, Lord Tennyson, as the greatest hymn ever written, to "The Old Rugged Cross," again and again voted by twentieth-century radio audiences the most popular of popular songs, Mr. Daugherty has captured the quality and significant message of these hymns and made of them living pictures—not literal illustrations, but rather interpretations of the spirit of the hymns. And it is the uniqueness, the genius of the great hymn that, whether written now or a thousand years ago, if it is destined for immortality, it must have a message that in any time breaks the Bread of Life for hungry hearts and anguished spirits.

Within the generations of those who shall read these lines, hymnology has received the attention of new schools of musical and spiritual intellectuals. Contributions have been made to the worship of the Church that place every worshipper in the debt of these trained and inspired educators in their chosen field. To mention only one, the Westminster Choir School, first of Dayton, Ohio, and now of Princeton, New Jersey, has become the center of a new generation of choir leadership and the inspiration for a new era in sacred song. A lost dignity has been restored and the majestic themes of the early Church have been revived and given new life in the worship of our time. It may be possible to sanctify "jazz" for particular times and places, but the sanctuary itself had too often become a musical temple of horrors when this new era dawned.

On the other hand, it is a misfortune for evangelical worship that in some scholarly places the gospel hymn is despised. Some educators "in marble palaces apart," to their own loss and to the hurt of the congregations, have dismissed entirely the gospel song. It is a distinct loss to evangelical tone and evangelistic quality that songs of the character Moody and Sankey popularized and carried to the ends of the earth, and to whose number Chapman and Charlie Alexander added a notable contribution, are not appreciated and used. Now in this broad field Homer Rodeheaver, more than any other song leader of his generation, has made community singing with religion at its heart the people's choice.

As this volume goes to press, a distinguished religious journal carries an article with stinging criticism of the training in worship that left "three men on a raft" with nothing more helpful to sing than simple "jazz" hymns. These fliers on a frail rubber craft, eight feet by four overall, covered more than one thousand miles in an incredible escape to a small inhabited island. Their escape is indeed "incredible," save for "God's mercy." The article continues as follows: "Not only did the men pray every day, but they sang such words as they could remember of 'When the Roll is Called Up Yonder,' and 'The Little Brown Church in the Vale.' What a travesty that they had no better help than these songs afforded! What an indictment of the type of religious instruction they had received. . . . Not very much strength or assurance for an hour of crisis!" The writer then expressed the conviction that such hymns as "O God, Our Help in Ages Past," or "We May Not Climb the Heavenly Steps," would have been much better had the fliers known them.

That particular article lacks even a sense of humor. God does not limit Himself to *a cappella* choirs, and for the men on the raft, the gospel hymn, the popular melody, the never-to-be-forgotten song of childhood, had infinite timeliness.

Our book is the demonstration of Paul's great text, "For he hath made us able ministers of the new testament: not of the letter, but of the spirit; for the letter killeth, but the spirit giveth life." The comprehensive worship of the sanctuary requires in its music flexibility. Everything, from "How Firm a Foundation," "O Love That Wilt Not Let Me Go," and "Lead Kindly Light," to "I'm a Child of the King," and from "A Mighty Fortress Is Our God," to "O Little Town of Bethlehem," and "The Battle Hymn of the Republic"—all of these and their contemporaries are required to bear the total message of the Cross, the redeeming grace of Calvary, and the glory of the resurrection hope.

Within these covers are.stories of the ages and pictures of their songs. Here march and counter-march the soldiers of the Cross who over all the earth have poured out their lives that life itself might be redeemed and sanctified. In the bravest moments of God's kingdom upon earth, men and women sang these songs, and from their voices came echoes that were as bugles of deliverance. Above the campfires of the Oregon Trail, in the sod houses of the prairies and in the log cabins of the remotest regions of America, the sons and daughters of a living faith turned from the labors and dangers of their day to find their comfort in "Rock of Ages." They sang such songs as "He Leadeth Me," not because they were afraid and not as children of retreat, but as searchers for the peace that passeth knowledge. They bowed upon their hasty altars before they slept—then rose at dawn and, singing, traveled on.

Now, in other times, when souls are tried and life is threatened, we remember their story, rejoice in their tradition, and hymn their songs to recover the amplitude of their faith. Once again we lift our streaming eyes to a cross and join the chorus of those who came up through great tribulation. With them we sing "I Need Thee Every Hour," and with them we unite in the universal anthem of the Christian Church:

> "All hail the power of Jesus' name!
> Let angels prostrate fall,
> Bring forth the royal diadem,
> And crown Him Lord of all."

To all who love the songs their mothers sang, and to all who sing the songs they themselves love, this book is dedicated.

DANIEL A. POLING

The Old Rugged Cross

There must be something very unusual about a gospel hymn that becomes the most popular "popular song" of its decade. However dear to the congregation of a Sunday morning sanctuary the music of worship may become, it is not to be expected that the crowd outside will entertain the same sentiments and emotions for such a program. But one hymn and only one, "The Old Rugged Cross," which swept through the revival meetings of its time, has been equally popular in secular audiences and on the air. Again and again it has ranked first among all melodies in all classifications listed in radio polls.

The author, George Bennard, was born of Scotch parentage in Youngstown, Ohio, February 4, 1873. His early life was not a prophecy of later religious distinction. His father conducted a saloon in a Michigan town and at a very early age George went to work in a coal mine. While the particulars of his career approaching manhood are unknown, in his youth he must have come under strong religious influences, for we find him as a young man joining the Salvation Army, and later conducting one of its campaigns in Bloomington, Illinois. Here he met and fell in love with Araminta Behler, a member of the Dutch Reformed Church. They were married and their life together became a united ministry for Christ.

George Bennard was a close student of the Scriptures who read widely in the field of religion and who enriched his study with constant prayer. For him always the Cross and its place at the heart of Christianity had a profound attraction. He accepted the Cross as central in God's plan of redemption. This acceptance is written into his song and again and again it is repeated in the four verses.

It was while he was meditating and studying that the theme of the song came to him, and with it the melody. He wrote the first line, "On a hill far away, stood an old rugged cross," but for weeks was unable to go on with the writing. As he expressed it, the voice of the Spirit seemed to say, "Wait." In a city of New York where he had gone to conduct a series of evangelistic meetings, he unpacked his bag with the thought, "In the privacy of my own room I shall continue the writing of my song." There he made the second attempt, but again it was impossible for him to go forward and again the voice of the Spirit seemed to say, "Wait." From his meeting in the State of New York he returned to Michigan and at last was able to finish the song.

Not only is this gospel hymn the most popular of our time, more frequently requested on the radio than any other, and with more phonograph records to its credit, but it has also won its place in the library of universal music. Its words have been translated into nearly every language and dialect and its melody may be heard as frequently in the jungles of Africa and on the islands of the Southern Pacific as in the camp meetings and churches of America.

I remember an evening at Chouir, in the Lebanon mountains high above the seaport city of Beirut, when a group of missionaries, in a conference with Sunday School and Christian youth leaders, closed their more formal session with a half hour of music. A young Arab clergyman, son of one of the earliest Christian families of Transjordania, read a lesson from the New Testament and then called for "The Old Rugged Cross." We were not far from Jerusalem that night and Calvary seemed even nearer.

The Old Rugged Cross

George Bennard, 1873-

George Bennard

On a hill far a-way stood an old rug-ged cross, The em-blem of suf-f'ring and shame; And I love that old cross where the dear-est and best For a world of lost sin-ners was slain.

Chorus

So I'll cher-ish the old rug-ged cross, the old rugged cross, Till my tro-phies at last I lay down; I will cling to the old rug-ged cross, the old rug-ged cross, And ex-change it some day for a crown.

Oh, that old rugged cross, so despised by the world,
Has a wondrous attraction for me;
For the dear Lamb of God left His glory above
To bear it to dark Calvary.

In the old rugged cross, stained with blood so divine,
A wondrous beauty I see;
For 'twas on that old cross Jesus suffered and died
To pardon and sanctify me.

To the old rugged cross I will ever be true,
Its shame and reproach gladly bear;
Then He'll call me some day to my home far away,
Where His glory forever I'll share.

I Love to Tell the Story

Katherine Hankey, 1834-1911

William G. Fischer, 1835-1912

I love to tell the story Of un-seen things a-bove, Of Je-sus and His glo-ry, Of Je-sus and His love. I love to tell the sto-ry, Be-cause I know 'tis true; It sat-is-fies my long-ings As noth-ing else can do.

Refrain

I love to tell the sto-ry, 'Twill be my theme in glo-ry, To tell the old, old sto-ry Of Je-sus and His love. A-men.

I love to tell the story;
More wonderful it seems
Than all the golden fancies
Of all our golden dreams.
I love to tell the story,
It did so much for me;
And that is just the reason
I tell it now to thee.

I love to tell the story;
'Tis pleasant to repeat
What seems, each time I tell it,
More wonderfully sweet.
I love to tell the story,
For some have never heard
The message of salvation-
From God's own holy Word.

I love to tell the story,
For those who know it best
Seem hungering and thirsting
To hear it like the rest.
And when, in scenes of glory,
I sing the new, new song,
'Twill be the old, old story
That I have loved so long.

I Love to Tell the Story

This lovely and popular hymn is taken from the heart of a poem of fifty stanzas, written in 1866 by Miss Katherine Hankey, the daughter of a London banker. The poem was on the life of Jesus and was in two parts, the first being entitled "The Story Wanted," and the second "The Story Told." From the first part was taken the well-known hymn "Tell Me the Old, Old Story." The companion hymn, which is our selection, is from Part II. These songs and others by the same author have been published from time to time in different forms and sometimes accompanied by tunes she composed.

This hymn was written during the author's convalescence after a long illness. It reveals the meditative mood. It is individual and introspective. The poet has been focusing the eyes of her spirit on things above. She has been feasting her soul upon the bread of life and finding strength that is not dependent upon any physical bloodstream. She has caught the significance, captured the unique quality of the story she tells. "For those who know it best seem hungering and thirsting to hear it like the rest." It is the story of which we never tire. Hers was the divine dissatisfaction that may be freshly satisfied in each hour and for each new experience. Again and again it is discovered that when one singer sings for the soul's desire or praise or fulfillment, he has sung for others, and so in the generations since Katherine Hankey wrote her poem, unknown millions have made it their song, each singing:

"I love to tell the story."

The tune was composed by William Gustavus Fischer, who was a native of Baltimore, Maryland, and a member of the firm of Gould and Fischer, dealers in pianos. While he resided in Philadelphia, he wrote some of the most popular of modern tunes for Sunday School, social gatherings, and evangelistic services.

Holy, Holy, Holy

Alfred, Lord Tennyson, poet laureate of England, declared "Holy, Holy, Holy," to be "the world's greatest hymn." Written when Reginald Heber was twenty-six years of age, it translates into majestic beauty the young vicar's vision of a congregation, great or small, or of a vast multitude united in worshipful song. While Heber wrote throughout his long and eventful life, the majority of his hymns appeared while he resided in the town of Hodnet, England, where for sixteen years he was the beloved pastor. He was a graduate of Oxford; while an undergraduate there, he won the university prize for Latin verse. Speaking of his sixteen years as a vicar, where he served as both parson and squire, Thackeray has written, "The charming poet, the happy possessor of all sorts of gifts and accomplishments . . . he was the beloved priest of his own home. . . . counselling the people in their troubles, advising them in their difficulties, kneeling often at their sick beds, sometimes at the hazard of his own life . . ."

Twice before accepting that great trust, he was called to be Bishop of Calcutta. He preferred not to go abroad, but he recalled his second refusal, believing that he had been disobedient to his heavenly vision. Heber's death in India came with tragic suddenness on Monday, April 3, 1826. On Sunday St. John's Church, Trichinopoly, was crowded to its utmost capacity for the confirmation of forty-two native Christians. In the morning the bishop delivered a message that became a spiritual tradition for the Christian community in that far center of Brahmanism. He completed the day with visits to the sick and the evening prayers. Then in the morning of the next day he was drowned while bathing. It is said that sudden immersion in cold water caused the breaking of a blood vessel in his head.

Of Reginald Heber's fifty-nine hymns nearly all are still being sung. Second only to "Holy, Holy, Holy," in the esteem of the church, is his immortal missionary hymn, "From Greenland's Icy Mountains." "Holy, Holy, Holy" is a metrical paraphrase of Revelations 4: 8-11. Line 2, stanza 1, "Early in the morning, our song shall rise to Thee," has been subject to several changes to adapt the hymn to any hour of the day. Some of the alterations are: "Grateful our adoring song," "Morning and evening our song," "Holy, Holy, Holy, our song," "Morning, noon, and night, our song."

Of Bishop Heber, who died at forty-three, it may be written that the immortal hymn which he gave to mankind is the song of his own spirit and the spiritual biography of his own soul.

The hymn tune is "Nicaea," by John Bacchus Dykes (1823-1876), master composer of three hundred hymn tunes. In addition to this tune, perhaps the best known of his compositions are "Lux Benigna" and "Cecelia," to which are set respectively "Lead Kindly Light" and "The King of Love My Shepherd Is."

Holy, Holy, Holy

Reginald Heber, 1783-1826

John B. Dykes, 1823-1876

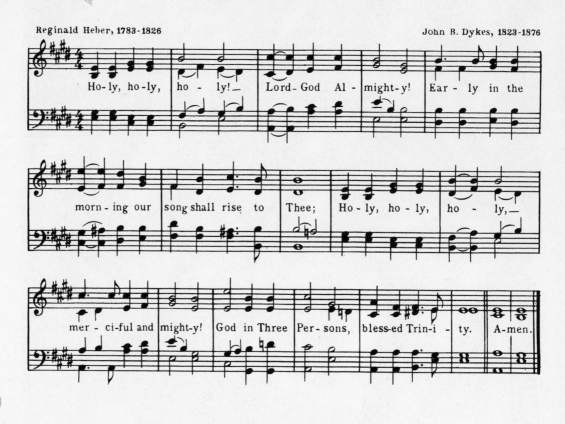

Holy, ho-ly, ho-ly! Lord God Al-might-y! Ear-ly in the morn-ing our song shall rise to Thee; Ho-ly, ho-ly, ho-ly,— mer-ci-ful and might-y! God in Three Per-sons, bless-ed Trin-i-ty. A-men.

Holy, holy, holy! All the saints adore Thee,
    Casting down their golden crowns around the glassy sea;
Cherubim and seraphim falling down before Thee,
    Which wert, and art, and evermore shalt be.

Holy, holy, holy! Though the darkness hide Thee,
    Though the eye of sinful man Thy glory may not see;
Only Thou art holy; there is none beside Thee,
    Perfect in power, in love, and purity.

Holy, holy, holy! Lord God Almighty!
    All Thy works shall praise Thy name, in earth, and sky and sea;
Holy, holy, holy, merciful and mighty!
    God in Three Persons, blessed Trinity!

Abide With Me

Henry F. Lyte, 1793-1847

William H. Monk, 1823-1889

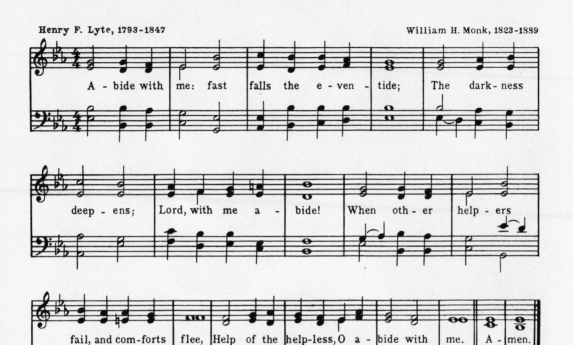

A-bide with me: fast falls the e-ven-tide; The dark-ness deep-ens; Lord, with me a-bide! When oth-er help-ers fail, and com-forts flee, Help of the help-less, O a-bide with me. A-men.

Swift to its close ebbs out life's little day;
Earth's joys grow dim, its glories pass away;
Change and decay in all around I see;
O Thou, who changest not, abide with me.

I need Thy presence every passing hour;
What but Thy grace can foil the tempter's power?
Who, like Thyself, my guide and stay can be?
Thro' cloud and sunshine, Lord, abide with me.

I fear no foe, with Thee at hand to bless;
Ills have no weight and tears no bitterness.
Where is death's sting? Where, grave, thy victory?
I triumph still, if Thou abide with me.

Abide With Me

I have visited the ancient seaport town of Brixham in Devonshire, England, where William of Orange landed and where, in a later time, one of America's great novelists, Honoré Willsie Morrow, made her home. I have stood upon the fishing docks, loaded with their harvest from the sea, and listened to the auctioneer cry his sales. I have watched the sunset from the surrounding hills and heard the stories of the past. Of these one of the loveliest is the story of Henry Francis Lyte, the village pastor who loved his garden and who, after a long illness, was torn from it to make a journey to Italy, where it was hoped he would recover his failing health. It was at this time, and perhaps with a sense of foreboding, that he wrote "Abide With Me."

The author was a native of Ednam, Scotland, born June 1, 1793, and graduated from Trinity College, Dublin. An orphan and poor, he first planned to become a physician. His parishioners in Brixham were simple fisher folk and soldiers from the nearby garrison. He came to the south of England, not only assuming a task overburdened with work, but giving up the cultural and social life that he greatly enjoyed, to follow completely the way of the Cross.

Although Lyte wrote music for his hymn, the tune which is most popular is "Eventide," composed by William Henry Monk. This is Monk's best-known composition. He was for many years a director of music at St. Matthias at Stoke Newington, and musical editor of *Hymns Ancient and Modern*. He is recognized as an authority on hymns.

The author of these profoundly moving words was his own severest critic. He refers to himself as having been worldly-minded until three years after he entered the ministry of the Church of England. It was at the bedside of a dying clergyman that he came into a personal experience of religion. Searching the Scriptures to find peace for his brother, he also found it for himself. "I was greatly affected," he wrote, "by the whole matter and brought to look at life and its issues with a different eye than before; and I began to study my Bible and preach in another manner than I had previously done."

It was during the twenty-four years of his ministry in Brixham, which began in 1823, that he wrote nearly all of his hymns. Here, as he expresses it, "I made hymns for my little ones and hymns for my hardy fishermen and hymns for sufferers like myself,"—he was a victim of consumption. Preaching his last sermon before he began his ill-fated journey to Italy, he also administered the Holy Communion. It is said that the congregation received the sacred elements from his failing hands in deep emotion and with tear-filled eyes. From this service he went to his study and, as twilight faded into deeper darkness, he wrote his verses with the accompanying music. That journey to Italy was never completed. He died en route and was buried in the English cemetery at Nice, France.

One evening in a great August camp meeting of young people in Tampere, Finland, I listened to this hymn accompanied by the musical instruments of several church orchestras that had been united for the occasion. It was the evening of a crowded summer day—later we knew that it was sunset for a people's hope of peace. "The darkness deepens, Lord, with me abide! When other helpers fail, and comforts flee, Help of the helpless, O abide with me. . . . Change and decay in all around I see; O Thou, who changest not, abide with me."

It is this hymn of the unchangeable that has comforted and will comfort the anguished soul of the world.

Jesus, Lover of My Soul

Of this immortal hymn, by all human tests one of the greatest, one of the most sublime ever written, Henry Ward Beecher said, "I would rather have written that hymn than to have the fame of all the kings that ever sat on the earth." The poem was written one hundred years before it was brought to America for its most famous setting.

The author of the tune was Simeon B. Marsh, who lived in Amsterdam, New York, and taught music in the neighboring towns. He tells of how, one beautiful morning, while riding from Amsterdam to Johnstown, he was deep in thought when inspiration came to him. Dismounting, he sat under a tree and wrote the music which he entitled "Martyn." Written for other words, it was several years later that Dr. Thomas Hastings discovered that it was even better suited to "Jesus, Lover of My Soul." The tune "Hollingside" is used also frequently in America.

Many beautiful stories are told of the origin of this hymn, which, together with the Twenty-third Psalm, another has said, "voices the creed, the hope and the prayer of Christendom." When Charles Wesley wrote it he was thirty-two. One story associated with it tells of how Wesley narrowly escaped death on the stormy Atlantic. Another, of a bird that, pursued by a hawk, flew into the wind and sought shelter in Wesley's arms. And even though these and other tales may have no foundation in fact, they are pleasant to remember. We do know that "Jesus, Lover of My Soul" was written almost immediately after a great spiritual change came to the author in 1738, and was published within a few months of the official date given for the founding of Methodism—1739.

As a hymn writer, Charles Wesley is unique. He is credited with more than sixty-five hundred hymns and it is one of the miracles of poetic writing that so many of these rise to the highest degree of excellence. His songs are the breath and substance of his own experiences—his conversion, his marriage, his panic during an earthquake, his fears as the result of rumors of an invasion from France, the Gordon riots, festivals of the Christian Church and every great doctrine of the Christian faith. He draws upon striking scenes in scriptural history and from the death of friends. It has been remarked that the mantle of Dr. Watts fell upon him. He wrote for all ages, and his hymns for little children are no less timely and beautiful than his comfort songs for the aged. The flow of music from his soul never ceased until death overtook him, and now, "being dead, he yet speaketh." To many song writers we are indebted for a single great production and to some for a number of songs that are deathless, but the record of Charles Wesley in number and quality far surpasses that of all other writers. In his field his work is unique and he stands alone. (See the story of "Christ, the Lord, Is Risen Today" for further details about John Wesley.)

Jesus, Lover of My Soul

Charles Wesley, 1707-1788

Simeon B. Marsh, 1798-1875

Je-sus, Lov-er of my soul, Let me to Thy bos-om fly,
While the near-er wa-ters roll, While the tem-pest still is high:
Hide me, O my Sav-iour, hide, Till the storm of life is past;
Safe in-to the ha-ven guide; O re-ceive my soul at last! A-men.

Other refuge have I none;
　Hangs my helpless soul on Thee;
Leave, ah! leave me not alone,.
　Still support and comfort me:
All my trust on Thee is stayed,
　All my help from Thee I bring;
Cover my defenseless head
　With the shadow of Thy wing.

Thou, O Christ, art all I want;
　More than all in Thee I find:
Raise the fallen, cheer the faint,
　Heal the sick, and lead the blind.
Just and holy is Thy Name,
　I am all unrighteousness;
False and full of sin I am,
　Thou art full of truth and grace.

Plenteous grace with Thee is found,
　Grace to cover all my sin;
Let the healing streams abound;
　Make and keep me pure within.
Thou of life the Fountain art,
　Freely let me take of Thee:
Spring Thou up within my heart,
　Rise to all eternity.

America the Beautiful

Katharine Lee Bates, 1859-1929

Samuel A. Ward, 1847-1903

O beau-ti-ful for spa-cious skies, For am-ber waves of grain,— For pur-ple moun-tain maj-es-ties A - bove the fruit-ed plain! A - mer - i - ca! A - mer - i - ca! God shed His grace on thee, —— And crown thy good with broth-er-hood From sea to shin-ing sea. A - men.

Words used by permission of Mrs. George S. Burgess

O beautiful for pilgrim feet,
Whose stern, impassioned stress
A thoroughfare for freedom beat
Across the wilderness!
America! America!
God mend thine every flaw,
Confirm thy soul in self control,
Thy liberty in law.

O beautiful for heroes proved
In liberating strife,
Who more than self their country loved,
And mercy more than life!
America! America!
May God thy gold refine,
Till all success be nobleness,
And every gain divine.

O beautiful for patriot dream
That sees, beyond the years,
Thine alabaster cities gleam,
Undimmed by human tears!
America! America!
God shed His grace on thee,
And crown thy good with brotherhood
From sea to shining sea.

America the Beautiful

"America the Beautiful" has in recent years become one of the most popular, if not the most popular, of all our national songs. Other songs have their distinctive fine qualities, but also, in almost every instance, some accompanying defects that prevent them from being accepted as completely satisfactory. They may breathe the spirit of vengeance or of captious criticism in the mood of a particular time. They may have their small moments, but few, if any, escape the tragedy of being negative rather than positive. Katharine Lee Bates has written the great affirmation of our American story. It is a declaration of faith—faith in God, faith in America, faith in brotherhood and faith in our common humanity.

Katharine Lee Bates knew and loved the broad reaches of her continent, and within her soul she entertained only love for her fellow men. She was born in Falmouth, Massachusetts, in 1859, and graduated from Wellesley College in 1880. She taught mathematics, the classics, and English in the high school of Natick, Massachusetts, and then came to Wellesley as an instructor in Latin. In 1885 she began her distinguished career as teacher and professor of English literature in Wellesley College.

Miss Bates was widely traveled. She spent a year in England at Oxford, another year in France and Spain, and a third year in Switzerland, Egypt, Syria and Italy. These longer visits were supplemented by several summers of foreign study and travel. While she edited editions of English classics, those volumes to which she referred as "her very own" were her books of poems, stories and travels, as well as other books on English and American literature.

"America the Beautiful" was written in Colorado in the summer of 1893. It remained in the author's notebook for more than two years and was not printed until July, 1895, when it appeared in a denominational organ, *The Congregationalist.* The original poem was revised in 1904. The first musical setting was by Silas G. Pratt, printed in Part 2 of *Famous Songs,* published in 1895. Perhaps the most popular setting is "Materna" by Samuel Ward. Other composers have written music for these lovely words. Among these is one, preferred by many, by Charles S. Brown.

Perhaps the vast expanse of Colorado is responsible for the spacious mood of this anthem. Katharine Lee Bates was surrounded by "purple mountain majesties" and she sat high "above the fruited plain" when she wrote "America, America, God shed His grace on thee, and crown thy good with brotherhood from sea to shining sea." Then, too, it was inevitable that her thoughts should run to her own New England as she wrote of "liberating strife" and of those heroic men and women "who more than self their country loved, and mercy more than life." But it was from her own triumphant soul that she released the vision "that sees beyond the years thine alabaster cities gleam, undimmed by human tears." As no other anthem, no other national song, "America the Beautiful" is suitable to all occasions — religious, secular and patriotic. It gives expression to the noblest emotions and aspirations of the American people.

I'm a Child of the King

On Washington's birthday, 1877, in the *Northern Christian Advocate,* appeared a poem of six verses from the pen of Mrs. Hattie E. Buell— "I'm the Child of a King." The Reverend J. B. Sumner, a clergyman of the Wyoming, Pennsylvania conference of the Methodist Episcopal Church, saw the poem and gave it the musical setting which made it one of the most popular gospel hymns of its time.

Since this collection, though from the first choices of many men and women, is finally my selection, my mother's song, which comes to me from the gray dawn where memory begins, is my first choice. My affection for the song goes back to earliest childhood, for my mother sang it in the Oregon cottage where I was born. As Savilla Kring, she heard it first at Chautauqua, New York, and began singing it in 1878 or even earlier. She was the soprano soloist in the famous National Quartet which in the late seventies and early eighties of the last century toured camp meetings and assemblies of the Eastern and Atlantic seaboard States.

In 1881, after appearing with the quartet at Old Orchard, in Maine, Round Lake, in New York, and elsewhere, Savilla Kring came to Ocean Grove, New Jersey. Wherever she had sung she had popularized her favorite number, "I'm a Child of the King," and at Ocean Grove it was called for repeatedly. Several years ago, following a Sunday morning service in the great tabernacle, during which I had referred to my mother's appearance on those grounds, a venerable man told me of hearing her sing this hymn at the dedication of one of the pavilions.

The summer of 1881 was saddened by the illness and death of the nation's second martyred President, James G. Garfield, who was shot on July 2. At the time of Savilla Kring's visit to Ocean Grove, President Garfield was at Long Branch, New Jersey, where he had been taken in the hope that the ocean air would contribute to his recovery. At the request of some member of the Garfield family who had been deeply moved by this song, the young singer was driven to Long Branch, where she sang "I'm a Child of the King," for the dying President.

Savilla Kring became the wife of my father, a young minister in the old Evangelical Association, now the Evangelical Church, and went with him as a bride to the State of Oregon. There, far removed from the scenes of her own girlhood ministry, she had a radiant part in the home mission church of the Pacific Coast. She cradled her children to the strains of the great hymns, and with them she sang the old ballads; but of all her songs, the one that was best loved and never forgotten is this poignant, lovely offering of Hattie E. Buell and J. B. Sumner.

Sumner, born at Wyalusing, Pennsylvania, March 25, 1838, was educated at Wyoming Seminary. For a number of years he followed the profession of music teacher and conducted singing schools about the countryside. He also engaged in the mercantile business, but entered the active ministry in 1869. Having an exceptional voice, he was a member of the musical organization known as the Wyoming Conference Trio, which became popular in early Chautauqua centers. He served a number of pastorates and was at one time a Presiding Elder of the Methodist Church—in Methodism this title has now been superseded by that of District Superintendent.

While the original poem of Mrs. Buell had six verses, only four were used in the song which, as originally written, and first sung, was called "I'm *the* Child of *a* King."

I'm a Child of the King

Hattie E. Buell

John B. Sumner, 1838-1918

My Fa-ther is rich in hous-es and lands, He hold-eth the wealth of the world in His hands! Of ru-bies and diamonds, of sil-ver and gold, His cof-fers are full, He has rich-es un-told. I'm a child of the King, A child of the King: With Je-sus my Sav-iour I'm a child of the King. A-men.

My Father's own Son, the Saviour of men,
Once wandered on earth as the poorest of them;
But now He is pleading our pardon on high,
That we may be His when He comes by and by.

I once was an outcast stranger on earth,
A sinner by choice, and an alien by birth;
But I've been adopted, my name's written down,
An heir to a mansion, a robe, and a crown.

A tent or a cottage, why should I care?
They're building a palace for me over there;
Though exiled from home, yet, still I may sing:
All glory to God, I'm a child of the King.

All Hail the Power of Jesus' Name

It was Harriett Clark who, in a great convention of young people held in San Francisco, California, in 1931, first proposed that "All Hail the Power of Jesus' Name" should be called the "national anthem" of the Christian Church, and that always congregations in all lands should stand while singing it. "Mother" Clark also proposed that "All Hail the Power of Jesus' Name" be made the international anthem of world-wide Christian Endeavor.

The author, Edward Perronet, was born in a family of wealth, a descendant from French Protestants, and the son of an Anglican clergyman. He was an intimate friend of the Wesleys and joined them in their evangelical activities and revivals. It was Perronet who insisted that the Wesleys withdraw from the Anglican Church and found a new society. When the Wesleys refused to take this radical step, Perronet, with great courage, founded an independent church in Canterbury. Here he remained as pastor until his death. The words of this hymn first appeared in the *Gospel Magazine* in 1780.

The distinguished American author and editor, Amos R. Wells, writes of one incident in the life of the author, as follows:

"John Wesley wanted to hear Perronet preach, and Perronet, for some reason, would not preach before Wesley. One day, Wesley, seeing Perronet in the congregation, announced that he would preach the next morning. Perronet did not want to make a scene, so the next morning he mounted the pulpit, explained that he had not consented to preach and felt that he could not, but nevertheless he would give them the best sermon that had ever been delivered. Thereupon he opened the Bible, and read the Sermon on the Mount from beginning to end, and without a word of comment. A song and prayer finished the service."

While Perronet published three volumes of religious verse, only one of his poems, this hymn, became immortal. Many striking incidents are associated with the song. One of these is related to the experience of a missionary in India, the Reverend E. P. Scott, who visited a wild mountain tribe where the Gospel had never been preached. He was surrounded by the savage band who prepared to take his life. The missionary, who was also a violinist, began to play and sing in the native language "All Hail the Power of Jesus' Name." With eyes closed and prepared to die, he sang on. When he reached the third stanza, opening his eyes, he was amazed to see the spears drop from the hands of the savages, great tears streaming from their eyes. Scott was invited to their homes, and in their communities he spent nearly three years reciting to them "the power of Jesus' name." After a brief furlough to America, he returned and worked among these tribesmen until he died.

The tune "Coronation," which is the most popular for this hymn, was written by Oliver Holden, a carpenter born in Shirley, Massachusetts, who organized and conducted singing schools. The organ on which "Coronation" was first played may still be seen in the State House above the Common in Boston.

The English tune "Miles Lane" is now widely used in America. This is more difficult, but has a majestic and stately rhythm. It was composed by William Shrubsole, who became acquainted with Perronet during his Canterbury days.

The stanza, "O that with yonder sacred throng," etc., was added in 1787 by the Reverend John Rippon.

All Hail the Power of Jesus' Name

Edward Perronet, 1726-1792
John Rippon, 1751-1836

Oliver Holden, 1765-1844

All hail the power of Je-sus' Name! Let an-gels pros-trate fall; Bring

forth the roy-al di-a-dem, And crown Him Lord of_ all; Bring

forth the roy-al di-a-dem, And crown Him Lord _ of all. A-men.

Sinners, whose love can ne'er forget
   The wormwood and the gall,
Go, spread your trophies at His feet,
   And crown Him Lord of all;
Go, spread your trophies at His feet,
   And crown Him Lord of all.

Let every kindred, every tribe,
   On this terrestrial ball,
To Him all majesty ascribe,
   And crown Him Lord of all;
To Him all majesty ascribe,
   And crown Him Lord of all.

O that with yonder sacred throng
   We at His feet may fall!
We'll join the everlasting song,
   And crown Him Lord of all;
We'll join the everlasting song,
   And crown Him Lord of all.

Lead, Kindly Light

John Henry Newman, 1801-1890

John B. Dykes, 1823-1876

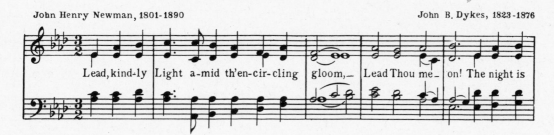

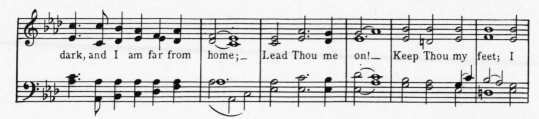

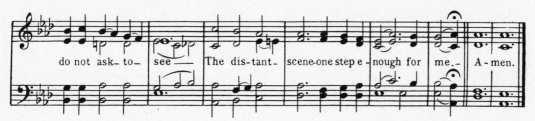

Lead, kind-ly Light a-mid th'en-cir-cling gloom,— Lead Thou me on! The night is dark, and I am far from home;— Lead Thou me on!— Keep Thou my feet; I do not ask to see— The dis-tant scene-one step e-nough for me.— A-men.

I was not ever thus, nor prayed that Thou
    Shouldst lead me on;
I loved to choose and see my path; but now
    Lead Thou me on;
I loved the garish day, and, spite of fears,
    Pride ruled my will: remember not past years.

So long Thy power hath blest me, sure it still
    Will lead me on,
O'er moor and fen, o'er crag and torrent, till
    The might is gone,
And with the morn those angel faces smile;
    Which I have loved long since, and lost awhile!

Lead, Kindly Light

"Lead, Kindly Light" was described by Hezekiah Butterworth, one of the recognized authorities on hymnology as "the sweetest and most trustful of modern hymns." Its author, John Henry Newman, was born February 21, 1801, and died in 1890. He was the son of a London banker. Ordained a clergyman of the Church of England in 1824, and made a vicar of St. Mary's Church, Oxford, 1828, he was one of the most popular and scholarly preachers of his time. Though he lived to a great age, he was never in robust health. While on the Continent seeking physical strength, he experienced a period of great spiritual unrest. It was during this time, and in the leadership of the Oxford movement, that he joined the Catholic Church. It was in this same period that he wrote "Lead, Kindly Light." Becalmed on the Mediterranean on June 16, 1833, he composed his immortal poem.

Dr. John B. Dykes is the author of the hymn tune, which, in contrast to the Mediterranean calm, was born on the Strand, one of London's most congested thoroughfares. Dr. Dykes was a clergyman of the Church of England who had great influence on church music in England and America.

Americans were given a new incentive to sing and love this song during the last illness of President McKinley, to whom it was of all songs the favorite. Born in one man's fervent, relentless prayer for light and guidance, this hymn has brought light and guidance to a vast multitude.

John Henry Newman wrote his poem twelve years before he was made a cardinal of the Roman Church. Its popularity is due at once to the theme of struggle for light and guidance and also to the triumphant note of absolute confidence in the final dawn. A great author has written of Newman's trip to Italy and his spiritual struggle, "He had no thought of becoming a Catholic, but was deeply grieved at the progress made by the liberal party in the English Church. . . . He met Catholics in Rome and went down alone to Sicily, where he was stricken with a fever, so that his servant thought he was dying. When he grew better, he set off across the Mediterranean for Marseilles. It was on this voyage, on June 16, 1833, that he wrote 'Lead Kindly Light'. . . . It was his prayer for leading in his perplexity that has become the prayer for guidance for a million saints."

Against the dark background of rival faiths and churches, torn by dissension, this song rises like a beacon of holy desire. Its language is the universal hunger of the soul that is restless until at last it rests in God. Beyond all divisions, here is the unity that is found in Christ.

Nearer, My God, to Thee

Sarah F. Adams, 1805-1848

Lowell Mason, 1792-1872

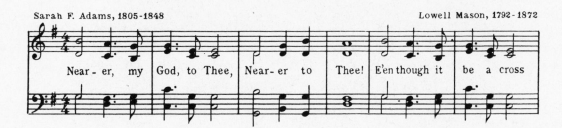

Near-er, my God, to Thee, Near-er to Thee! E'en though it be a cross

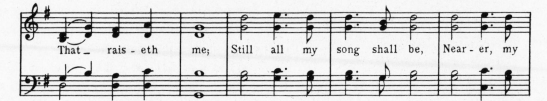

That rais-eth me; Still all my song shall be, Near-er, my

God, to Thee, Near-er, my God, to Thee, Near-er to Thee! A-men.

Though like the wanderer,
  The sun gone down,
Darkness be over me,
  My rest a stone;
Yet in my dreams I'd be
  Nearer, my God, to Thee,
  Nearer to Thee!

There let the way appear,
  Steps unto heaven;
All that Thou sendest me,
  In mercy given;
Angels to beckon me
  Nearer, my God, to Thee,
  Nearer to Thee!

Then, with my waking thoughts
  Bright with Thy praise,
Out of my stony griefs
  Bethel I'll raise;
So by my woes to be
  Nearer, my God, to Thee,
  Nearer to Thee!

Nearer, My God, to Thee

This hymn was heard over the world with a never before realized significance after the sinking of the *Titanic*. On that fateful night, as the great ship went to its doom and as passengers in high courage moved steadily into the lifeboats, the band played, "Nearer, My God, to Thee." And how near hundreds were! This hymn was another favorite of two American Presidents, Theodore Roosevelt and William McKinley.

The author, Mrs. Sarah Flower Adams, had been an actress, but ill health compelled her to give up her stage career. She turned then to literature, becoming a contributor to contemporary magazines. Her song has its foundation in Jacob's experience at Bethel.

The father of Sarah Adams was the editor of the *Cambridge Intelligencer* and her husband was a distinguished engineer. Her taste for literature was acquired very early in life, and also in her early life she came into a deep religious experience which made always an impression upon those who met her.

While President McKinley's favorite song was "Lead, Kindly Light," the words of this hymn, "Nearer, My God, to Thee," were the last upon his lips as he lay dying in Buffalo, New York. Mrs. Adams' song at once met with some favor, but it was not until Dr. Lowell Mason wrote for it the music that it became known throughout the world. In Philadelphia, in December, 1900, fifteen hundred trained voices made it their great convention hymn. When the singing ceased, a silence of profound awe held the vast congregation. It was then that President Eberman of the Pennsylvania Christian Endeavor Union rose and said, "I wonder if we shall ever listen to such singing on earth again."

Mrs. Adams turned instinctively to religious writing. In 1841 she published a dramatic poem, *Vivia Perpetua,* which dealt with the conflict of heathenism and Christianity, and in which Vivia Perpetua, an early Christian, suffered martyrdom. In 1845 she wrote *The Flock at the Fountain,* a catechism with hymns for children. As a member of the congregation of the Reverend W. J. Fox, a Unitarian minister in London, she contributed thirteen of her own productions to a volume, *Hymns and Anthems.*

The tune to which "Nearer, My God, to Thee" is almost invariably sung, written by Lowell Mason, is called "Bethany." As a young man he was leader of the church choir and director of music of the Bowdoin Square Church, Boston. Here he began his work with children and it was through him that the teaching of music was introduced in the public schools of Boston. This was the beginning of public school music in America.

Faith of Our Fathers

No hymn is more completely acceptable to all Christians than this, the greatest of all the poems by Frederick William Faber. It was written during the period of persecution when even attendance upon divine services was punishable by imprisonment. It came out of the period of passionate struggle in the life of the author.

Faber was an intimate friend of John Henry Newman, whom he followed into the Roman Catholic Church, and this hymn, when written, was designated "for singing and reading by loyal Catholics." How poignant was the ordeal through which Faber passed is indicated by the fact that before he left the Church of England, he wrote several articles in that Church's defense, and though his hymns were published after his withdrawal from it, practically all of his poetry was written before he made the revolutionary change.

Of his writing he had the following to say: "It was natural that an English son of St. Philip should feel the want of a collection of English Catholic hymns fitted for singing. The few in *The Garden of the Soul* were all that were at hand, and of course they were not numerous enough to furnish the requisite variety. As to translations, they do not express Saxon thought and feelings, and consequently the poor do not seem to take to them. The domestic wants of the Oratory, too, kept alive the feeling that something of the sort was needed, though at the same time the author's ignorance of music

appeared in some measure to disqualify him for the work of supplying the defect. Eleven of the hymns were written, most of them for particular tunes and on particular occasions, and became very popular with country congregations. They were afterward printed for the schools at St. Wilfrid's."

Faber also points in this same connection to Wesley's hymns as being the models which for simplicity and intense fervor he would endeavor to emulate. From this small book of eleven hymns his hymn writing finally resulted in a total of one hundred and fifty, all of which are found in his *Hymns* of 1862, and many of them in various Roman Catholic collections for missions and schools.

Faber was born at Calverley Vicarage, Yorkshire, on June 28, 1814, and educated at Balliol College, Oxford. He was graduated in 1836. For a time he was a fellow of the University College in the same institution. He took holy orders in 1837 and was made rector of Elton, Huntingdonshire, in 1843, but withdrew three years later to join the Church of Rome. In 1849 he established in London the Oratorians, or "Priests of the Congregation of St. Philip Neri." His death was on September 26, 1863.

The hymn tune, "St. Catherine," is a composition of Henri Frederic Hemy, and was altered later by James George Walton. Hemy, an English organist and compiler of music, also edited a pianoforte tutor.

FAITH ⨍ OUR FATHERS

Faith of Our Fathers

Frederick W. Faber, 1814-1863

Henri F. Hemy, 1818-1888
Adapted by James G. Walton, 1821-1905

Faith of our fa - thers! liv - ing still In spite of dun-geon, fire, and sword,

O how our hearts beat high with joy When-e'er we hear that glo-rious word! Faith of our

fa - thers, ho - ly faith! We will be true to thee till death. A - men.

Faith of our fathers! we will strive
To win all nations unto thee,
And through the truth that comes from God
Mankind shall then be truly free.
Faith of our fathers, holy faith!
We will be true to thee till death.

Faith of our fathers! we will love
Both friend and foe in all our strife,
And preach thee, too, as love knows how
By kindly words and virtuous life.
Faith of our fathers, holy faith!
We will be true to thee till death.

O Little Town of Bethlehem

Phillips Brooks, 1835-1893

Lewis H. Redner, 1831-1908

O lit-tle town of Beth-le-hem, How still we see thee lie! A-bove thy deep and dream-less sleep The si-lent stars go by; Yet in thy dark streets shin-eth The ev-er-last-ing Light; The hopes and fears of all the years Are met in thee to-night. A-men.

For Christ is born of Mary,
 And gathered all above,
While mortals sleep, the angels keep
 Their watch of wondering love.
O morning stars, together
 Proclaim the holy birth,
And praises sing to God the King,
 And peace to men on earth!

How silently, how silently
 The wondrous gift is given!
So God imparts to human hearts
 The blessings of His heaven.
No ear may hear His coming,
 But in this world of sin,
Where meek souls will receive Him still,
 The dear Christ enters in.

O holy Child of Bethlehem!
 Descend to us, we pray;
Cast out our sin, and enter in,
 Be born in us today.
We hear that Christmas angels
 The great glad tidings tell;
O come to us, abide with us,
 Our Lord Immanuel!

O Little Town of Bethlehem

The popularity of this exquisitely beautiful song of the birth of Christ is universal. From having been first a Christmas song of America, it has become, for childhood at least, the Christmas song of the world. There is no language where it is not known, no nation where it is not loved, and no people where it is not sung.

Phillips Brooks, the author, was born in Boston, Massachusetts, on December 13, 1835, where he died in January, 1893. Though he died in comparative youth, he remains as a preëminent figure of the American Church and one of the noblest spirits of the generations. He was a true poet, a wise administrator, an understanding friend of youth, a lover of little children, and an incomparable preacher. Graduating from Harvard in 1855, he completed his theological studies at Alexandria, Virginia. His first pastorate was in Philadelphia at the Church of the Advent, now Holy Trinity, in Rittenhouse Square. Here in 1868 he wrote "O Little Town of Bethlehem." Written for his own Sunday School, it was first used in the Christmas service of that year.

The tune, "St. Louis," is by Lewis Redner, organist of the church, superintendent of the Sunday School, and a teacher of one of the classes. Brooks came to Redner with what he called "a simple carol" and the setting was completed in a great hurry on the Saturday night before the Christmas service at which the song was first sung. For more than twenty years it was unknown to congregations, but by 1890 it had come into general use. Describing his experience in writing the music, Mr. Redner related that it was at midnight before the Christmas dawn that he awoke with the strains that were destined to become immortal, ringing in his ears. Taking music paper, he wrote the melody of the tune and, a few hours later, before going to his organ, filled in the harmony.

Phillips Brooks had an unusual preparation for his literary career. He was reared in a home where music and hymn study were compulsory, and had committed to memory more than two hundred hymns before he was twenty-one. Two years before he wrote this song he went to Palestine, visited Bethlehem, saw the fields where the shepherds watched and the cave of the Nativity. It was with the memory of this pilgrimage still fresh in his mind, and as the Christmas Day again approached, that he wrote his "little carol."

From the Philadelphia church he was called to Trinity in Boston, where the present beautiful structure was erected under his pastorate. In 1891, two years before his untimely death, he became Bishop of Massachusetts. By the great cathedral of worship which is in a sense his monument, stands his statue, executed by St. Gaudens, one of the most daring ever made. Brooks is represented in striking dynamic posture, while behind, with one hand resting upon his shoulder, is the Master, and overshadowing them rises the Cross.

Surely, no minister of the Gospel of Christ and no man in any calling has been more worthily remembered in bronze and stone, but long after church and monument have returned to the dust from which they came, the little carol upon the lips of little children, and with the voices of all ages, will ring out upon the Christmas morning, and while the world sings "O Little Town of Bethlehem" Phillips Brooks will be remembered.

O Love That Wilt Not Let Me Go

Many songs have been born in mortal pain or rise from an experience of tragedy in the souls of the authors. Such is the case with this hymn. It was written by George Matheson in the Manse of Inellan, Scotland, on June 6, 1882. He was alone on the day of his sister's marriage, his family being in Glasgow and spending the night there. That night of mystery to the world was one of intense suffering to the pastor. Something happened, known only to himself and never related by him to a living soul, that left him with an anguished spirit, but out of which came to the Christian Church one of its noblest and most poignant hymns. It has been said that it was "the quickest thing he had ever done in his life." It came to him as though dictated. It was written in five minutes and never corrected.

Twenty years before this poem was written, Matheson became blind, but already he had yielded his "flickering torch" to the "great companion" who never failed to guide his steps aright. "O light that followest all my way" was for the author more than a poetic fancy. For him it was the realism of Christian experience, and in George Matheson's experience a vast multitude, men and women of all faiths and ages in all the years since he wrote, have been comforted. It is said that, on one occasion when he preached before Queen Victoria, she, thanking him for the sermon, expressed her greater indebtedness for the song.

It is the last verse that has for every tortured spirit the promise of triumph and the prospect of peace. "O Cross that liftest up my head, I dare not ask to fly from Thee; I lay in dust, life's glory dead, and from the ground there blossoms red Life that shall endless be."

The author was born at Glasgow, March 27, 1842, and, in spite of the blindness which came to him in early youth, graduated from the University of Edinburgh in 1862 with a brilliant record. He became parish minister at Inellan in 1868 and was later stationed at St. Bernard's in Edinburgh. He was the Baird Lecturer in 1881 and St. Giles Lecturer in 1882. He was the author of important prose works. His death came suddenly on August 28, 1906.

The tune for Matheson's hymn was written by Dr. Albert L. Peace, Glasgow organist and musical editor of *The Scottish Hymnal of 1885.* It was a strange custom of Dr. Peace to carry about with him words of hymns for which he wrote notes as the tune would come to him. It was in 1884, on the sands of Arran, an island off the west coast of Scotland, that he read the words of "O Love That Wilt Not Let Me Go," and immediately he had the setting. The transcription took several minutes only.

O Love That Wilt Not Let Me Go

George Matheson, 1842-1906   Albert L. Peace, 1844-1912

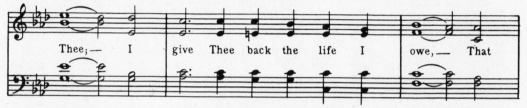

O Love that wilt not let me go, — I rest my weary soul in Thee; — I give Thee back the life I owe, — That in Thine o-cean depths its flow May rich-er, full-er be. A-men.

O light that followest all my way,
I yield my flickering torch to Thee;
My heart restores its borrowed ray,
That in Thy sunshine's blaze its day
May brighter, fairer be.

O joy that seekest me through pain,
I cannot close my heart to Thee;
I trace the rainbow through the rain,
And feel the promise is not vain
That morn shall tearless be.

O Cross that liftest up my head,
I dare not ask to fly from Thee;
I lay in dust, life's glory dead,
And from the ground there blossoms 'red
Life that shall endless be.

I Need Thee Every Hour

Annie S. Hawks, 1835-1918

Robert Lowry, 1826-1899

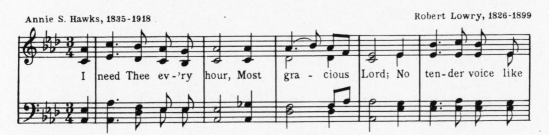

I need Thee every hour;
  Stay Thou near by;
Temptations lose their power
  When Thou art nigh.

I need Thee every hour,
  In joy or pain;
Come quickly and abide,
  Or life is vain.

I need Thee every hour;
  Teach me Thy will;
And Thy rich promises
  In me fulfill.

I Need Thee Every Hour

This intimate hymn comes out of the mystical experience of the one who wrote it—Annie Sherwood Hawks. She relates that while busying herself in her room one day, she became aware of what she described as "the nearness of my Master." She felt definitely that she was not alone in the chamber. There came over her not only the sense of His presence, but the realization that she needed and desired the presence constantly, that there was not a waking moment of her life when she wished to be absent from her Lord. The very words of this hymn, "I need Thee every hour," ran through her mind and possessed it, and immediately she sat down to write. It was as though someone sang as she wrote. She gave the verses to her pastor, the Reverend Robert Lowry, who composed for it the tune we know as "Need."

Mrs. Hawks is described as a "quiet, dignified lady with a face that shone with divine peace." She was born in Hoosic, New York, May 25, 1835, and was for many years a resident of Brooklyn. She contributed hymns to many song publications of the day—*Bright Jewels, Pure Gold, Royal Diadem, Temple Anthems,* etc. Among her poems are, "I Need Thee Every Hour," written in April, 1872; "Thine, Most Gracious Lord"; "Why Weepest Thou? Whom Seekest Thou?" and many others of the same spirit and form. She died in 1918.

Robert Lowry, the composer of the tune, was a man of many distinctions. Born in Philadel-phia on March 12, 1826, he was educated at Bucknell University, Lewisburg, Pennsylvania. Ordained a Baptist minister, his first charge was at West Chester, Pennsylvania. He preached in churches in New York City and in Brooklyn, and in 1876, at the age of fifty, was appointed Professor of Rhetoric of his alma mater. Later he again served as a pastor. He is associated with some of the most popular Sunday School hymn books, and of his own productions the following are among those that have been widely circulated and used:

"Low in the Grave He Lay"
"One More Day's Work for Jesus"
"Shall We Gather at the River?"
"Where Is My Wandering Boy Tonight?"

Perhaps no American composer of his period whose activities ceased half a century ago is still so generously represented in the hymnology library of the Christian church.

The appeal of the chorus—"I need thee, O I need thee, every hour I need thee," is one of the most poignant ever written into a sacred song. I have heard it in the trained cultured voice of a twentieth-century prima donna, and in the burdened tones of a humble man before a mission altar of prayer. It is equally effective wherever sung, for its quality is such that it suits the mood of the human heart, wherever the cry of the heart is raised. The hymn is as constant as every hour and as universal as the love of Christ.

Just As I Am

Charlotte Elliott has the distinction of writing what is generally regarded as the greatest of all evangelistic compositions. In results, it is a comprehensive course in Christian theology. Evangelical and conservative, it is also as broad as the love of God revealed in Jesus Christ. Dwight L. Moody said of this hymn, "it has done the most good to the greatest number and has touched more lives helpfully than any other hymn."

Charlotte Elliott was born in a family of culture and received what was, for her time and for a young woman, a remarkable education. Two of her brothers were clergymen. Although she lived to the advanced age of eighty-two, she became an invalid at thirty-two. It was in the early years of her illness that she became acquainted with the great Dr. Caesar Malan, and to this friendship may be attributed much of the spiritual quality and depth to be found in her verses. It was Dr. Malan who asked her to give her life completely to her Lord and who, when she said that she did not know how to find Him, replied, "Come to Him just as you are."

An intimate friend of the family, in describing Charlotte, said: "Her ill health often caused her the peculiar pain of seeming useless while the lives of those about her were filled with service. It was in such a time of trial and while she lived at Westfield Lodge, Brighton, that her brother, the Reverend H. V. Elliott, conceived the plan of St. Mary's Hall, Brighton, a school designed to give at nominal cost a high education to the daughters of clergymen. . . . In aid to this project there was to be a bazaar. . . . Westfield Lodge was all astir. Every member of the large circle was busy morning and night with the one exception of the ill sister. She was as eagerly interested as any, but not physically fit. The night before the bazaar she was kept wakeful by distressing thoughts of her apparent uselessness. These thoughts passed by transition to imagination and spiritual conflict, till she questioned the reality of her whole spiritual life and wondered whether it was anything better than an illusion of the emotions. The next day the troubles of the night came back with such force that she felt they must be met and conquered. She gathered up in her soul the grand certainties, not of her emotions, but of her salvation: her Lord, His power, His promise; and taking pen and paper, deliberately set down in writing for her own comfort, the formula of her faith. . . . She restated to herself the gospel of pardon and peace. . . . As the day wore on, her sister-in-law came to see her and to bring news of the work. The poem was ready, a copy was asked for. So it came out of the quiet room into the world."

Now for more than one hundred years beyond the quiet room it has ministered to unnumbered millions. The brother who founded the college has written of the song, "In the course of a long ministry I hope I have been permitted to see some fruit of my labors, but I feel far more has been done by this one hymn of my sister's."

Charlotte Elliott was described as "a lover of nature, a lover of souls and a lover of Christ."

William Bachelder Bradbury (1816-1868) composed the music of this hymn, as he did of "He Leadeth Me" and of many other religious songs.

Just As I Am

Charlotte Elliott, 1789-1871

William B. Bradbury, 1816-1868

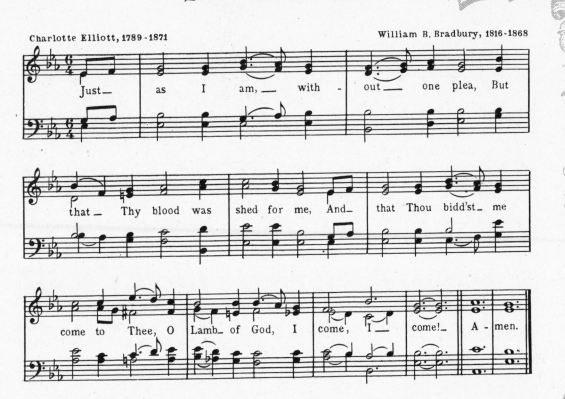

Just as I am, without one plea, But that Thy blood was shed for me, And that Thou bidd'st me come to Thee, O Lamb of God, I come, I come! A-men.

Just as I am, and waiting not
To rid my soul of one dark blot,
To Thee whose blood can cleanse each spot,
O Lamb of God, I come, I come!

Just as I am, though tossed about
With many a conflict, many a doubt,
Fightings and fears within, without,
O Lamb of God, I come, I come!

Just as I am, poor, wretched, blind;
Sight, riches, healing of the mind—
Yea, all I need, in Thee to find,
O Lamb of God, I come, I come!

How Firm a Foundation

"K" in Rippon's Selection, 1787

From John F. Wade's Cantus Diversi, 1751

How firm a foun-da-tion, ye saints— of the Lord,— Is laid for your faith— in His ex-cel-lent Word! What more can He say than to you He hath said,— To you—who for ref-uge to Je-sus have fled?— To you — who for ref-uge to Je-sus have fled? A-men.

"Fear not, I am with thee; O be not dismayed,
For I am thy God, and will still give thee aid;
I'll strengthen thee, help thee, and cause thee to stand,
Upheld by my righteous, omnipotent hand,
Upheld by my righteous, omnipotent hand..

"When thro' the deep waters I call thee to go,
The rivers of woe shall not thee overflow;
For I will be with thee, thy troubles to bless,
And sanctify to thee thy deepest distress,
And sanctify to thee thy deepest distress.

"When through fiery trials thy pathway shall lie,
My grace, all-sufficient, shall be thy supply,
The flame shall not hurt thee; I only design
Thy dross to consume, and thy gold to refine,
Thy dross to consume, and thy gold to refine.

How Firm a Foundation

"How Firm a Foundation" was the favorite hymn of many famous men, among them Robert E. Lee, Theodore Roosevelt, and Woodrow Wilson. It was sung at the funeral service of each of these great Americans. In it is direction to the Source of all strength and the assurance of God's presence when earthly help has failed. The Bible is the firm foundation and when the deep waters and the rivers of sorrow threaten to overwhelm, we are assured that the flood shall not overflow and that our deepest distress will be turned to our good.

The author of the hymn is anonymous, but it first appeared in a collection published by Dr. John Rippon, *Selections*, 1787. Dr. Rippon was one of the most popular and influential dissenting ministers of his time. From 1790 to 1802 he published the *Baptist Annual Register*. This was a periodical covering the most important contemporary events in the history of the Baptist denomination in Great Britain and America. It is even now a valuable reference work.

While the hymn is anonymous as first printed, the author was indicated by the letter "K" and it is generally believed that the "K" stood for Robert Keen, a member of Dr. Rippon's church.

The tune, though generally credited to the Portuguese, is probably English in origin. The Duke of Leeds named it the "Portuguese Hymn" because he first heard it in the Portuguese Chapel in Leeds, but Vincent Novello, organist at the Portuguese Chapel, ascribed the tune to John Reading. Here Amos R. Wells disagrees, saying: "It is the music of a Latin Christmas hymn, 'Adeste Fideles,' a hymn which we have translated in the familiar 'O Come, All Ye Faithful.' "

Dr. Wells tells of how Andrew Jackson, retiring from the presidency, became a devout member of the Presbyterian Church. One day in his old age he spoke to a company of visitors as follows: "There is a beautiful hymn on the subject of the exceeding great and precious promises of God to his people. It was a favorite hymn of my dear wife till the day of her death. It begins thus: 'How firm a foundation, ye saints of the Lord.' I wish you would sing it now."

The Sunday School Times once carried a story of General Curtis Guild, Jr., as follows: "The Seventh Army Corps was encamped on the hills above Havana, Cuba, on Christmas Eve, 1898. Suddenly a sentinel from the camp of the Forty-ninth Iowa called, 'Number ten; twelve o'clock, and all's well!' A strong voice raised the chorus and many voices joined in until the whole regiment was singing. Then the Sixth Missouri added its voice and the Fourth Virginia, and all the rest, till there, as General Guild said, 'on the long ridges above the great city a whole American army corps was singing:

'Fear not, I am with thee, O be not dismayed;
For I am thy God, and will still give thee aid;
I'll strengthen thee, help thee, and cause thee
    to stand,
Upheld by My righteous, omnipotent hand.'

Protestant and Catholic, South and North, singing together on Christmas day in the morning!"

Onward, Christian Soldiers

This is the greatest of all marching songs for peace or war. It has every mood of those who march and suits every circumstance of human emotion. "Onward, Christian Soldiers" has an invitation, a dynamic impulse to be found in no other marching number. It is equally acceptable to the bagpipes and the trumpets. On occasion, the most distinguished musical organizations and the humblest bands of small communities alike find it appropriate.

One afternoon in Suva, the Fiji Islands, while our great ship waited for its tourists to assemble, I watched the governor and his party, surrounded by a great company of well-wishers, board the vessel that was to carry him from his old post to a new and more distinguished assignment. Upon the dock were grouped the native soldiers, the island military organizations with their colorful band. Several numbers had been played and of course the last strains we heard as presently we moved out into the channel were those of "God Save the King." But again and again that day it was "Onward, Christian Soldiers," that brought the people to a high pitch of emotion. They had marched to it from the governor's house down to the shore and they had cheered to it as the governor stood waving his hand upon the deck high above the multitude.

The hymn was written for a Sunday School festival. The author, Sabine Baring-Gould, a clergyman, was both deeply religious and definitely independent. He was also born with great musical and poetic gifts. Confronted with the task of taking his Sunday School scholars to their meeting place in a neighboring town, and knowing the mischievous character of the boys,

he knew, too, that singing would help keep them straight on their journey. Finding no song that suited his immediate purpose, he sat down and wrote this one. The children loved it, sang it all the way, and with it made of their trip a great lark. The world has been singing it and marching to it ever since.

The music with which "Onward, Christian Soldiers" is best known was written by Sir Arthur Sullivan, "St. Gertrude." It was first sung and used by the author to the slow movement of Haydn's Symphony in D.

Baring-Gould's love story is most unusual and romantic. When he met his future wife, she was the daughter of a mill worker. He sent her off to college and, when she graduated, married her. He himself pronounced the marriage vows! The marriage was completely happy and at her death her husband inscribed on her tomb these words: "Half my soul." (For further details about Baring-Gould, see the story of "Now the Day Is Over.")

Arthur Sullivan's father was a bandmaster at the Royal Military College, Sandhurst, in England, and the boy's musical talent was such that before he was eight years old he had learned to play almost every wind instrument in the band. Also at this early age he composed his first piece, "By the Waters of Babylon." He was given a thorough training and became organist at St. Michael's, Chester Square, in 1861. Six years later he moved to St. Peter's. He wrote many anthems and hymns. His last tune was composed, by command, for Queen Victoria's diamond jubilee in 1897.

Onward, Christian Soldiers

Sabine Baring-Gould, 1834-1924   Arthur S. Sullivan, 1842-1900

On-ward, Christian sol-diers March-ing as to war, With the cross of Je-sus Go-ing on be-fore. Christ, the roy-al Mas-ter, Leads a-gainst the foe; For-ward in-to bat-tle, See His ban-ners go!

Refrain

On-ward, Chris-tian sol-diers, March-ing as to war, With the cross of Je-sus Go-ing on be-fore. A-men.

Like a mighty army
　Moves the Church of God;
Brothers, we are treading
　Where the saints have trod;
We are not divided,
　All one body we,
One in hope and doctrine,
　One in charity.

Crowns and thrones may perish,
　Kingdoms rise and wane,
But the Church of Jesus
　Constant will remain;
Gates to hell can never
　'Gainst that Church prevail;
We have Christ's own promise,
　And that cannot fail.

Onward, then, ye people,
　Join our happy throng,
Blend with ours your voices
　In the triumph song;
Glory, laud, and honor,
　Unto Christ the King;
This through countless ages
　Men and angels sing.

[51]

O Master Let Me Walk with Thee

Washington Gladden, 1836 - 1918

H. Percy Smith, 1825 - 1898

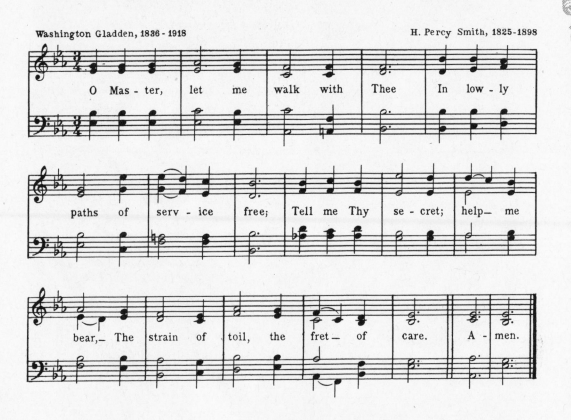

O Mas-ter, let me walk with Thee In low-ly paths of serv-ice free; Tell me Thy se-cret; help me bear,— The strain of toil, the fret of care. A-men.

Help me the slow of heart to move
By some clear, winning word of love;
Teach me the wayward feet to stay,
And guide them in the homeward way.

Teach me Thy patience; still with Thee
In closer, dearer company,
In work that keeps faith sweet and strong,
In trust that triumphs over wrong;

In hope that sends a shining ray
Far down the future's broadening way;
In peace that only Thou canst give,
With Thee, O Master, let me live.

O Master, Let Me Walk with Thee

The author of this hymn, Washington Gladden, was pastor of the First Congregational Church in Columbus, Ohio, when I came to that city as a young student minister. Though advanced in years, he was still a dynamic personality and the most distinguished citizen of the community. I remember him well: a great head upon shoulders slightly bowed and a patriarch's beard that marked him as one of the fathers. Several times I heard him speak and twice I sat with him in the study of his church. On one of these occasions, he made clear and emphatic his reasons for refusing support to an evangelistic campaign that was to bring to the city one of the most popular but eccentric evangelists of the generation. He did not object to the emphasis upon personal decisions, he said. He believed in decision. But he did object to what he regarded as an over-emphasis upon personal evangelism or an emphasis which, in his opinion, would subordinate the social message of the Church. Also, he was afraid that the campaign would strengthen one class against another and withdraw the Church from the under-privileged. I felt then that he was mistaken, but I could not mistake his spirit and purpose. He was still a warrior for the weak, and what a warrior!

As a leader in all religious movements for social reform and as the greatest voice of his time for the social gospel, Gladden was greatly criticized. This hymn reflects the conflict of his militant ministry. It is his own prayer cry for "patience" and for the "winning word of love." He realized his need of these, for as often as he was rebuked by others he was self-rebuked, and all that he preached to his people, who adored him, he related to himself. Beyond the moment, with its conflict and misunderstanding, he looked "far down the future's broadening way," and claimed for himself, as for those he served, the peace that is the Master's gift to those who with the Master live.

Washington Gladden's immortal hymn is worthily called the anthem of social progress, the hymn of Christian service.

The author was born in Pottsgrove, Pennsylvania, February 11, 1836. He was educated at Williams College. Entering the Congregational ministry, he became one of the most famous of the educators and clergy of his church. He was editor of the *New York Independent,* and of the *Sunday Afternoon.* It was in the latter publication that this hymn appeared in March, 1879, in the devotional section called "The Still Hour." Perhaps the first two stanzas suggest Washington Gladden's sense of responsibility as a pastor. The song throughout is a prayer hymn, and the author strongly felt that it should be used in its own time and season.

The tune, "Maryton," or "Sun of My Soul," was the setting which Dr. Gladden desired. It was composed by Canon Henry Percy Smith, an English clergyman. It is an interesting contrast upon fame that, in his time, Canon Smith was not a famous musician. Now in Dr. Gladden's hymn his fame is established and made secure.

He Leadeth Me

The author of "He Leadeth Me," Joseph H. Gilmore, was the son of a governor of New Hampshire. The hymn was written after a service conducted in the First Baptist Church, Philadelphia. The author had been explaining the meaning and beauty of the Twenty-third Psalm to the congregation and, born in the emotions of that service, the theme of the hymn was later developed in the home of Deacon Wattson. Gilmore wrote while those about him engaged in conversation.

He was associated with the University of Rochester for many years and was a professor emeritus at the time of his death in 1918. The poem first appeared in the *Watchman and Reflector,* where William B. Bradbury found it and in 1863 composed the tune by which it is known throughout the world. Bradbury was a composer of popular Sunday School and church music. Also, he was known as a manufacturer of pianos and other musical instruments.

It is altogether possible that the poem would never have been published had not Gilmore's wife appreciated its real value and forwarded it to the paper. Referring to this fact, Dr. Gilmore said, "As I wrote the hymn, the refrain consisted of only two lines. Mr. Bradbury added the other two. In all other respects it stands just as I wrote it in Wattson's parlor. . . . I did not know until 1865 that it had been set to music. I went to Rochester to preach as a candidate before the Second Baptist Church. In their chapel on the day that I reached the city, I took up a hymnal to see what they sang and opened it at my own hymn, 'He Leadeth Me.' I accepted it as an indication of divine guidance and have no doubt I was right." This statement first appeared in the Philadelphia *Public Ledger.*

Dr. Gilmore's chair in Rochester University was Logic. He was a graduate of Brown University, where he received the degree A.B., and of Newton Theological Institution. At Newton he was Professor of Hebrew in 1861-62.

On the site of the old First Baptist Church in Philadelphia, now occupied by a modern business structure, is a bronze tablet telling the story of the composing of this noble song which comes from the most comforting of all psalms. It was not a Sunday morning service of the sanctuary, but a prayer meeting, that gave this gracious ministry to the world. As the preacher read the ancient message and commented upon it to the people, he was caught up even as men of the faith in ancient times and given a vision of things celestial. The vision stayed, and in the home of a friend was transferred to the written page. It is for us a "blessed thought" that Joseph Gilmore was "led" to write this hymn that shall never die.

This song is associated with many intimate religious gatherings I have attended. Again and again I have heard it in the prayer meetings of my own churches and called for it in the Quiet Hours of youth conferences. I remember a Sunday morning in the Far West when a veritable downpour threatened to break up the eleven o'clock service in the round tent. The congregation was small and the preacher uncertain of what the next few minutes would produce. It was then that one of the small group seated on the rough benches began singing, "He leadeth me, O blessed thought, O words with heavenly comfort fraught; whate'er I do, where'er I be, still 'tis God's hand that leadeth me." Before the song was finished and while the small cloudburst still thundered upon the canvas, the preacher was sure of himself and of his message, and the service became filled with the power of the Holy Spirit.

He Leadeth Me

Joseph H. Gilmore, 1834-1918

William B. Bradbury, 1816-1868

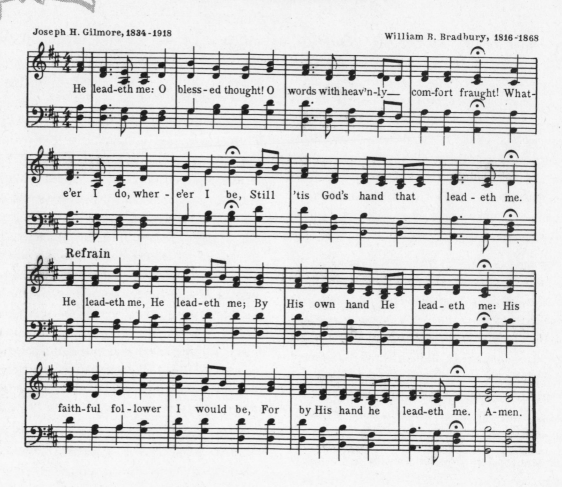

He lead-eth me: O bless-ed thought! O words with heav'n-ly— com-fort fraught! What-e'er I do, wher-e'er I be, Still 'tis God's hand that lead-eth me.

Refrain

He lead-eth me, He lead-eth me; By His own hand He lead-eth me: His faith-ful fol-lower I would be, For by His hand he lead-eth me. A-men.

Sometimes 'mid scenes of deepest gloom,
Sometimes where Eden's bowers bloom,
By waters calm, o'er troubled sea,
Still 'tis His hand that leadeth me.

Lord, I would clasp Thy hand in mine,
Nor ever murmur nor repine;
Content, whatever lot I see,
Since 'tis my God that leadeth me.

And when my task on earth is done,
When, by Thy grace, the victory's won,
E'en death's cold wave I will not flee,
Since God through Jordan leadeth me.

Now the Day Is Over

This song was written for the children of England. The author, the Reverend Sabine Baring-Gould, was a clergyman and pastor whose very soul was in his Sunday School. While he wrote for the nation, he had particularly the children of his own church in mind. The theme is taken from verses in the Book of Proverbs. In his day there was a distinct need for children's hymns and for hymns to be sung in the evening. "Now the Day Is Over" was given its place in the evening services of his congregation.

The tune, "Merrial," was composed by Joseph Barnby, and the low pitched notes give it a quality particularly fitted to the evening service of song. Joseph Barnby wrote nearly two hundred and fifty hymn tunes. He had a sense of mission, believing that he was called to contribute better music to the service of the Church. This tune is largely upon one note and yet the rich chords prevent monotony.

Sabine Baring-Gould was the oldest son of Edward Baring-Gould of Lew Trenchard, Devon, in England. He was born at Exeter, January 25, 1834, and died in 1924. He was educated at Clare College, Cambridge, where he received his B.A. in 1854 and his M.A. in 1856. He took holy orders in 1864 and held the curacy of Horbury, near Wakefield, until 1867, when he went to Dalton, Yorkshire. In 1871 he became rector in East Mersea, Essex, and in 1881 of Lew Trenchard. He wrote volumes of sermons, and many other works. His hymns, original and translated, appeared in the *Church Times* and the *People's Hymnal.* Among the most popular of his productions are "Onward, Christian Soldiers" (see the story of this hymn), "Daily, Daily, Sing the Praises," and the Easter hymn, "On the Resurrection Morning."

As a very small boy, I remember "Now the Day Is Over" from my father's church in the West. I was always impressed with the third verse, "Grant to little children visions bright of Thee; guard the sailors tossing on the deep blue sea." Even now I remember the emotion produced by those last words, "on the deep blue sea," and often when I have moved out upon the ocean or flown high above it, I have remembered the singing children of the church in my boyhood valley. No song ever written has been so conducive to both physical and spiritual relaxation and repose as "Now the Day Is Over."

Now the Day Is Over

Sabine Baring-Gould, 1834-1924

Joseph Barnby, 1838-1896

Now the day is o - ver, Night is draw-ing nigh, ___ Shad - ows of the eve - ning Steal a - cross the sky. A - men.

Jesus, give the weary
  Calm and sweet repose;
With Thy tenderest blessing
  May mine eyelids close.

Grant to little children
  Visions bright of Thee;
Guard the sailors tossing
  On the deep blue sea.

Through the long night watches,
  May Thine angels spread
Their white wings above me,
  Watching round my bed.

Crown Him With Many Crowns

Matthew Bridges, the author of this hymn, was the youngest son of John Bridges, Wellington House, Surrey, and a brother of the Reverend Charles Bridges, who was the author of *An Exposition of the 119th Psalm.* He was born at The Friars, Maldon, Essex, England, on July 4, 1800, and though educated in the Church of England, became a member of the Church of Rome.

His many works include: *Babbicombe, or Visions of Memory, With Other Poems,* 1842; *Hymns of the Heart,* 1848 (enlarged in 1852); and *The Passion of Jesus,* 1852.

His more popular hymns are taken from his later works and the greater number of these from *Hymns of the Heart.* The songs from his pen which are found in American collections were introduced through the Plymouth Collection of 1855, compiled by Henry Ward Beecher. The most acceptable of these are:

"Lo, He Comes with Clouds Descending"
"Rise, Glorious Conquerer, Rise"

"Head of the Hosts in Glory"
"Bright Were the Mornings First
    Impearl'd"
"Soil Not Thy Plumage, Gentle Dove"

Matthew Bridges came to the Province of Quebec in Canada and died there in his ninety-fifth year, on October 6, 1894. His writings always sound a note of profound spirituality. They have power and majesty. At least four hymns now in common use open with Bridges' "Crown Him with Many Crowns" and all of these are based upon the hymn which first appeared in his book, *The Passion of Jesus.* It was then titled, "The Song of the Seraphs."

Sir George J. Elvey composed the tune "Diademata" for this hymn and it appeared in *Hymns Ancient and Modern* in 1868. Elvey was born in Canterbury, England, in 1816. He was organist of St. George Royal Chapel, Windsor, from 1835 to 1883, and received the degree of Doctor of Music from Oxford in 1840. He was knighted in 1871.

Crown Him With Many Crowns

Matthew Bridges, 1800-1894

George J. Elvey 1816-1893

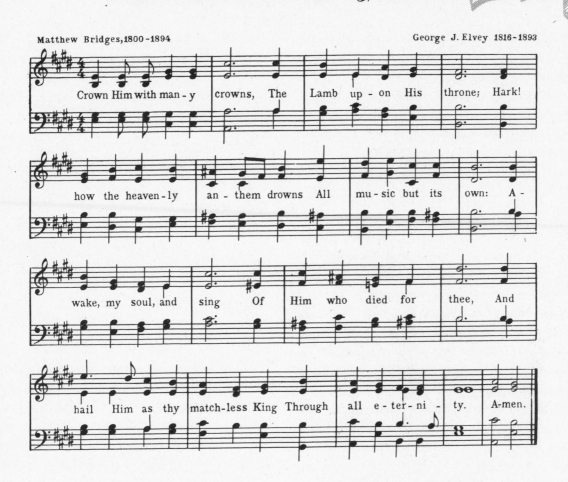

Crown Him with man-y crowns, The Lamb up-on His throne; Hark! how the heaven-ly an-them drowns All mu-sic but its own: A-wake, my soul, and sing Of Him who died for thee, And hail Him as thy match-less King Through all e-ter-ni-ty. A-men.

Crown Him the Lord of love:
　Behold His hands and side,
Rich wounds, yet visible above,
　In beauty glorified:
No angel in the sky
　Can fully bear that sight,
But downward bends his burning eye
　At mysteries so bright.

Crown Him the Lord of peace;
　Whose power a scepter sways
From pole to pole, that wars may cease,
　Absorbed in prayer and praise:
His reign shall know no end;
　And round His pierced feet
Fair flowers of Paradise extend
　Their fragrance ever sweet.

Crown Him the Lord of years,
　The Potentate of time;
Creator of the rolling spheres,
　Ineffably sublime:
All hail, Redeemer, hail!
　For Thou hast died for me:
Thy praise shall never, never fail
　Throughout eternity.

Silent Night, Holy Night

Of all the immortals who have sung this most famous of Christmas hymns, perhaps Madame Ernestine Schumann-Heink brought to it the greatest distinction of voice and character. It became a very part of her and though she was queen of unnumbered roles in opera and the most popular concert singer of her time, "Silent Night, Holy Night" was the best-loved of all her songs.

It happened that the great diva on one occasion appeared in Kansas City, Missouri, during the sessions of an International Christian Endeavor Convention. Following her own program, very graciously she consented to sing for the thousands of young people in the local convention hall, and of course she sang "Silent Night, Holy Night." As a presiding officer on that never-to-be-forgotten evening, I introduced the famous guest singer. In presenting her as a surprise for the convention, I told the story of meeting her son, George Washington Schumann-Heink, during World War I. George, her youngest child, was with the A. E. F., and when I became acquainted with him was a convalescent in Toul, France. Deeply moved, Madame Schumann-Heink expressed her appreciation and gratitude by singing once again this immortal song. As she left the auditorium with tear-filled eyes, she turned, waving her farewells.

I well remember, too, the first Christmas occasions of my childhood. The Christmas tree would be carried in by my father. A few years later, I would assist him. And then, on Christmas morning, after the children of the house had all been washed and breakfasted—the breakfast was a hurried, inconsequential meal—the door would be opened, and with the youngest leading the way, and parents bringing up the rear, the family would rush to the tree. The decorations were simple—popcorn and cards, perhaps a few candles, but the tinsel and colored balls of these times were all lacking in that pioneer community.

There would be at least one present for each of the nine children. The first present I recall was a Noah's ark. It was nearly the death of me, for I tried to digest the paint. The second was a beautiful knife and a third a copy of *Uncle Tom's Cabin*. But one thing never failed on those Christmas mornings of long ago. Always my mother sang and led the children in singing "Silent Night, Holy Night," and she would sing the German words, "Stille Nacht, Heilige Nacht."

Joseph Mohr, the author, wrote this hymn on Christmas eve, 1818, at a meeting in the Arnsdorf schoolhouse in Austria. He was surrounded by friends, but withdrew for a short time, and later, with the presenting of gifts, handed to his friend Franz Gruber a single sheet of paper upon which he had written the beautiful words of this poem.

Tyrolese singers first made the song famous throughout Germany and Austria. The author was born at Salzburg, Austria, on December 11, 1792. He was ordained a priest on August 21, 1815, and served successively in a number of congregations. He was not quite fifty-six years of age when he died on December 4, 1848. It is interesting to know that it was a young clergyman who wrote the words of the hymn and his friend, a young schoolmaster, who set it to music. Franz Gruber, the schoolmaster was born November 25, 1787, at Hochburg, near Linz. He was the organist at Hallein, near Salzburg, at the time of his death, June 7, 1863.

Silent Night, Holy Night

Joseph Mohr, 1792-1848

Franz Gruber, 1787-1863

Si - lent night, ho - ly night, All is calm, all is bright;
Round yon Vir - gin Moth- er and Child! Ho-ly In-fant, so ten-der and mild,
Sleep in heav- en-ly peace, Sleep in heav- en-ly peace. A - men.

Silent night, holy night,
Darkness flies, all is light;
Shepherds hear the angels sing,
"Alleluia! hail the king!
Christ the Saviour is born,
Christ the Saviour is born."

Silent night, holy night,
Son of God, love's pure light;
Radiant beams from Thy holy face,
With the dawn of redeeming grace,
Jesus, Lord, at Thy birth,
Jesus, Lord, at Thy birth.

Silent night, holy night,
Wonderous Star, lend Thy light;
With angels let us sing,
Alleluia to our King;
Christ the Saviour is born,
Christ the Saviour is born.

When I Survey the Wondrous Cross

The author of this noble hymn, Isaac Watts, has been called the "father of English melody." There are still many churches where the hymns of Watts predominate, and for years in England worshippers would sing no other hymns than his. In the hymnal of the writer's denomination, there are twenty-three of Watts' hymns and fifteen of the author next approaching him, Charles Wesley.

Watts was born in Southampton, England, July 17, 1674. He died at the age of 74, in November, 1748. His father maintained a popular school to which students came from the British colonies, particularly from America and the West Indies. The strange commentary upon the religious life of the time to which the son contributed so much is the fact that the father, soon after the birth of Isaac, was imprisoned for non-conformity.

The boy studied languages at an early age and was a precocious reader. He became pastor of the Independent Church, in Mark Lane, 1702, after having served as an assistant for four years. Although ill health greatly disturbed his ministry, he continued to preach for nearly fifty years. His later home was with Sir Thomas Abney, where a planned short stay was extended over thirty years.

"When I Survey the Wondrous Cross" is the most popular of this great writer's songs. It appeared in his own volume *Hymns and Spiritual Songs,* 1707, an enlarged edition of which came out in 1709. George Whitefield was the first to popularize the four-stanza form, and it is in this form that "When I Survey the Wondrous Cross" has achieved its world-wide popularity. It is generally regarded as one of the four preëminent hymns of the English language. The taste of the author for verse appeared early in childhood. He had as his teacher Mr. Pinhorn, who was the rector of All Saints' and headmaster of the Grammar School in Southampton. So impressive were the lad's accomplishments that he was offered help to secure an education in one of the great universities, looking toward ordination in the Church of England. However, he was quite independent and entered the non-conformist Academy. At the age of twenty he left school, and in the next two years, while at home, the greater number of his *Hymns and Spiritual Songs,* to which we have already referred, were written. The degree of Doctor of Divinity bestowed on him in 1728 by the University of Edinburgh was quite unusual, since in Britain, then as now, honorary degrees were not at all so incidental as they are in America. He is one of the few to be buried in a Puritan cemetery—at Bunhill Fields—with a monument in Westminster Abbey. He was a theologian and philosopher as well as a poet, and his work on *The Improvement of the Mind* is eulogized by Dr. Johnson. For generations his *Logic* was an Oxford textbook.

The tune is called "Hamburg" and comes from Gregorian chants. Gregory was born in Rome, and during the appalling plagues, without thought of risk to himself, visited the suffering and dying, singing messages of hope. Lowell Mason arranged the tune in the form known to us.

When I Survey the Wondrous Cross

Isaac Watts, 1674-1748   Lowell Mason, 1792-1872

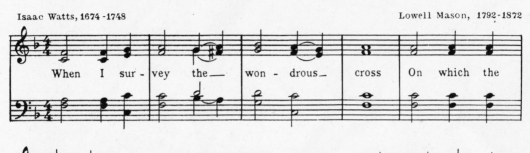

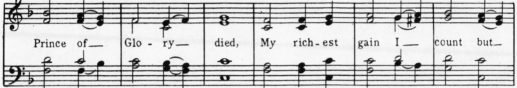

When I survey the wondrous cross On which the Prince of Glory died, My richest gain I count but loss, And pour contempt on all my pride. A-men.

Forbid it, Lord, that I should boast,
Save in the death of Christ, my God:
All the main things that charm me most,
I sacrifice them to His blood.

See, from His head, His hands, His feet,
Sorrow and love flow mingled down:
Did e'er such love and sorrow meet,
Or thorns compose so rich a crown?

Were the whole realm of nature mine,
That were a present far too small;
Love so amazing, so divine,
Demands my soul, my life, my all.

Fairest Lord Jesus

While this exquisitely beautiful song is called "The Crusaders' Hymn," we now know that the crusaders did not use it in their journeys toward the Holy City. It is possible that German pilgrims on their way to Jerusalem may have sung it, since it was written in 1677. Also, it has been associated with a group of German children who were attached to the ill-fated Children's Crusade. As these boys and girls moved across the plains and mountains of Europe and pressed toward the Holy Land, the name of Jesus was ever on their lips and it was of Him that they sang. They suffered incredible hardships and never reached their goal, but this song remains as, in a sense at least, their gift to the ages, and their memorial.

It was not published in America until 1850, when Richard Storrs Willis released it. It has become one of the most popular numbers of young people's conferences and has a central place in the worship services of the Church. Nothing more beautiful has ever been contributed to the ministry of sacred music.

The tune with which we are familiar was arranged by Richard Storrs Willis from a Silesian folk song. Of it he says, "How far back this melody goes cannot be determined. It is sung by all classes and all ages and by the shepherd on the hillside and the lisping urchin in the nursery."

Willis, a journalist and musician, was born in 1819 and died in 1900. He was the son of Deacon N. Willis, the founder of the *Youth's Companion,* which for generations was the most popular young people's publication in America.

I have listened to "The Crusaders' Hymn" and lifted my own halting voice in its melody on the continents of both hemispheres. I have heard young people sing it in the twilight services among western mountains and by eastern lakes. Once at a summer camp in Czechoslovakia, after a Quiet Hour service in which I had spoken to the radiant youths of a new freedom, my soul was swept by this hymn lifted in adoration. The boys and girls of that never-to-be-forgotten evening are scattered. The tree-shaded field where they met has been swept by the machines of war, but the spirit in which they sang is invincible, and many more times will voices sing there "Fairest Lord Jesus, ruler of all nature."

Fairest Lord Jesus

From the German, 17th century

Richard S. Willis, 1819-1900

Fair - est Lord Je - sus, Rul - er of all na - ture, O Thou of

God and man the Son, Thee will I cher - ish,

Thee will I hon - or, Thee, my soul's Glo - ry, Joy, and Crown. A - men.

Fair are the meadows,
Fairer still the woodlands,
Robed in the blooming garb of spring:
Jesus is fairer,
Jesus is purer,
Who makes the woeful heart to sing.

Fair is the sunshine,
Fairer still the moonlight,
And all the twinkling starry host:
Jesus shines brighter,
Jesus shines purer
Than all the angels heaven can boast.

Rock of Ages

Augustus M. Toplady, 1740-1778

Thomas Hastings, 1784-1872

Rock of A - ges, cleft for me, Let me hide my-self in Thee; Let the
wa - ter and the blood, From Thy wound - ed side which flowed, Be of
sin the dou - ble cure, Save from wrath and make me pure. A - men.

Could my tears for ever flow,
Could my zeal no languor know,
These for sin could not atone;
Thou must save, and Thou alone:
In my hand no price I bring;
Simply to Thy cross I cling.

While I draw this fleeting breath,
When my eyes shall close in death,
When I rise to worlds unknown,
And behold Thee on Thy throne:
Rock of Ages, cleft for me,
Let me hide myself in Thee.

ROCK OF AGES

Rock of Ages

On the western plains of the North American continent, "Rock of Ages" was a favorite song of the pioneers. With the covered wagons drawn up at night in a great circle and with campfires burning brightly, the men and women of that sturdy time would gather with their children for evening prayers. Upon the canopy of night this hymn would rise, and in the Rock of Ages those who faced the uncertainties of the morrow, the hidden dangers of the trail, would find their comfort and safety. To a great company this hymn of Augustus Montague Toplady is first among all others, and Dr. Charles S. Robinson declared it to be the supreme hymn of the language.

It is said that the author, born in 1740, came to a profound religious experience at the age of sixteen while sitting in an English barn listening to a man preach who could not write his name. Soon after this eventful night Toplady entered Trinity College, Dublin. After graduation he became a priest, but his ministry lasted through only ten years. A victim of consumption, he died in 1778, at the age of 38. As a preacher he was unusually brilliant and had exceptional social qualities. In spite of his illness, he referred to himself as the happiest man in the world. Far from being disturbed at the thought of death, he was anxious for the event and said, "It will not be long before God takes me, for no mortal can live after the glories which God has made manifest to my soul."

This, the greatest of his productions, came directly from theological controversy, and was written in the opening year of the American Revolution—1776. Toplady and John Wesley were theological opponents and their debate joined in the dogma of election. "Rock of Ages, cleft for me," rises from that debate, though, as it has survived, the discussion will live in the hearts of men beyond all controversies. Prince-Consort Albert, the husband of Queen Victoria, as he lay dying, repeated, "Rock of Ages, cleft for me."

The hymn tune, entitled "Toplady," was written by Thomas Hastings. Hastings was born in Connecticut and later led the village choir in Clinton, New York, the seat of Hamilton College. Later, New York churches united and called him as the leader of their choirs. He wrote six hundred hymns and one thousand hymn tunes. At one time he edited a musical paper in Utica, New York.

Dear Lord and Father of Mankind

John Greenleaf Whittier, the great New England Quaker poet, sang always for the common people. He was a country boy who knew and loved the farm. Determined to secure an education, he worked toward this end, and at the age of nineteen had saved enough money to attend Haverhill Academy for two seasons. Whittier was one of the first Abolitionists, though he would not have chosen the name. Many of his finest poems· are written about the evils of slavery and his whole life was devoted to freeing the slaves. His great hymn is a fervent prayer for personal purity and unselfishness.

Whittier was born at Haverhill, Massachusetts. on December 17, 1807, and died at Hampton Falls, New Hampshire, September 17, 1892. On the farm he learned the trade of shoemaker and later became a successful journalist and editor, in addition to his distinction as a poet. At various times he edited the *American Manufacturer,* the *New England Review,* and, on becoming secretary of the American Anti-Slavery Society, the *Pennsylvania Freeman.* He was for a time a contributing editor of the *National Era.* The majority of his later works were written after he moved to Amesbury, Massachusetts, in 1840.

He never thought of himself as a hymn writer and even after his poems were used extensively by congregations, he said of himself, "I am not a hymn writer for the good reason that I know nothing of music. Only a few of my pieces were written for singing. A good hymn is the best use to which poetry can be devoted. But I do not claim to have succeeded in composing one." However, the most competent critics affirm that Whittier's "pieces" are characterized by rare and rich poetic beauty, poignant tenderness and unfaltering sympathy for the oppressed.

Although John Greenleaf Whitter was a Quaker, he was spiritually a militant and his writings had their part in sending men into one of the greatest of all conflicts for human freedom. He never sought to evade the issue of moral responsibility and, though he never wore a sword or carried a gun, he bore his part in the War Between the States. He was one of those heroic spirits who accept the inevitable and to whom new occasions teach new duties.

My old New Hampshire home was founded by another Quaker family that in 1776 made a choice not unlike Whittier's spiritual decision. The sons of the great house went down from their New England hilltop to give their lives for liberty and each man made his own decision. One can imagine their return when the war was over and the unity of their faith in the prayer:

"Dear Lord and Father of mankind,
  Forgive our fev'rish ways;
Re-clothe us in our rightful mind;
  In purer lives Thy service find,
  In deeper rev'rence praise."

Frederick C. Maker, who was born in 1844, a composer of many hymn tunes and anthems, wrote "Elton," the tune used for Whittier's hymn. He died in 1927.

Dear Lord and Father of Mankind

John G. Whittier, 1807-1892

Frederick G. Maker, 1844-1927

Dear Lord and Fa - ther of man - kind, For - give our fev' - rish ways! Re - clothe us in our right - ful mind; In pur - er lives Thy serv-ice find, In deep-er rev' - rence, praise.

In simple trust like theirs who heard,
Beside the Syrian sea,
The gracious calling of the Lord,
Let us, like them, without a word,
Rise up and follow Thee.

O Sabbath rest by Galilee!
O calm of hills above,
Where Jesus knelt to share with thee
The silence of eternity,
Interpreted by love!

Drop Thy still dews of quietness,
Till all our strivings cease;
Take from our souls the strain and stress,
And let our ordered lives confess
The beauty of Thy peace.

Sun of My Soul

The author of this majestic hymn was a professor of poetry at Oxford for ten years before he became rector of Hursley Church. As a pastor, he kept open house day and night, the doors of the sanctuary swung wide. Of fine and cultured tastes, he was quite unassuming and in his parish the poor regarded him as their best friend.

As a child he was taught by his father, and entered college at the age of fourteen. He earned the highest honors ever attained in England by one so young.

This hymn reflects the author's constant love of nature and is suggestive, too, of the early training of his Christian home.

He became professor of poetry at Oxford in 1881 and it was at the death of his father and under the influence of his father's life that he returned to the Church to continue as the vicar of Hursley for the last thirty years of his life. His poems are a famous collection called *The Christian Year*.

A famous musical director remarks that John Keble is hardly to be called a hymn writer, and supports the position by calling attention to the fact that few of his verses have come into popular collections of hymns for worship. The criticism is justified in part at least, for it is true that often his verses are detached from their context, so that their signification is seriously affected. On the other hand, if we accept the word "hymn" in the wider sense as "a song of adoration to some supreme being," which is Dr. Johnson's definition, then John Keble is one of the supreme figures among great writers. In this field he is the very master of "delicate and refined thoughts, expressed in the most delicate and refined language," and today, nearly a hundred years after he wrote, nearly a hundred of his productions are in general use. A few of these, of which "Sun of My Soul" is the most famous, are acknowledged as among the finest and most popular in their language.

"Hursley" is the tune to which these words are generally sung. It is, of course, the name of the parish in which the author spent more than a quarter of a century in his ministry and where he is buried. Peter Ritter, the composer, was born in 1760 and died in 1846. He was a native of Mannheim, Germany, and became chapel master to the Grand Duke of Baden in 1811.

Sun of My Soul

John Keble, 1792-1866

Adapted from Katholisches Gesangbuch, c. 1774

Sun of my soul,— Thou Sav - iour dear, It is not night— if Thou— be near: O may no earth - born cloud a - rise To hide Thee from Thy ser - vant's eyes. A - men.

When the soft dews of kindly sleep
My wearied eyelids gently steep,
Be my last tho't, how sweet to rest
For ever on my Saviour's breast.

Abide with me from morn till eve,
For without Thee I cannot live;
Abide with me when night is nigh,
For without Thee I dare not die.

If some poor wandering child of Thine
Have spurned, today, the voice divine,
Now, Lord, the gracious work begin;
Let him no more lie down in sin.

My Faith Looks Up to Thee

Ray Palmer, 1808-1887

Lowell Mason, 1792-1872

My faith looks up to Thee, Thou Lamb of Cal - va - ry,

Sav - iour di - vine! Now hear me while I pray, Take all my

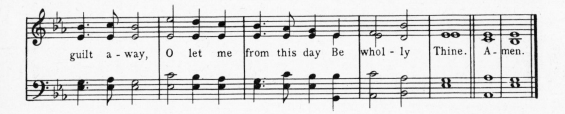

guilt a - way, O let me from this day Be whol - ly Thine. A - men.

May Thy rich grace impart
Strength to my fainting heart,
My zeal inspire;
As Thou hast died for me,
O may my love to Thee
Pure, warm and changeless be,
A living fire!

While life's dark maze I tread,
And griefs around me spread,
Be Thou my guide;
Bid darkness turn to day,
Wipe sorrow's tears away,
Nor let me ever stray
From Thee aside.

When ends life's transient dream,
When death's cold, sullen stream
Shall o'er me roll;
Blest Saviour, then, in love,
Fear and distrust remove;
O bear me safe above,
A ransomed soul!

My Faith Looks Up to Thee

The son of Dr. Ray Palmer, who wrote "My Faith Looks Up to Thee," describes his father as "thoroughly conscientious and honest, with a sensitive nature always under control—a loyal friend and a generous opponent." This hymn, which is found in practically every hymnal of the Christian Church, was written in the quiet of the pastor's study and with no thought that any other eyes would ever see it. For two years it was carried about in the author's pocket and then one day Dr. Lowell Mason of Boston, who was publishing a book of hymns, asked Dr. Palmer to furnish a number. Taking the original from his pocket, Palmer made a copy for his friend. On returning to his home, Dr. Mason, deeply impressed with the poem, read it again and again and then sat down and immediately composed for it the tune "Olivet."

Ray Palmer was born in Little Compton, Rhode Island, on November 12, 1808, and died March 29, 1887. Entering the ministry, he preached in a Congregational church in Bath, Maine, for fifteen years. After some time spent in travel in 1850, he became pastor of the First Congregational Church of Albany, New York.

Sixteen years later he was the corresponding secretary of the American Congregational Union in New York City. His later years were spent in literary and general pastoral activities.

Mark Hopkins said of him that in philosophy and moral science he was one of the best-read men of his time. This, his greatest work, is associated with his own ill health and religious uncertainty and it voices the vision of faith which came out of his darkness. Just before he composed the verses, he had translated a German poem which described a suppliant at the Cross, and as he rewrote the description, there came to him a vision of Christ.

Lowell Mason, the author of the tune, also wrote the setting for Bishop Heber's noble missionary hymn, "From Greenland's Icy Mountains." He was in Savannah, Georgia, at the time. Returning to Boston, he made music his life work. He became president of the Handel and Haydn Society and later founded the Boston Academy of Music. He is described as the one "who did more to improve and elevate American church music than any other man."

Come, Thou Almighty King

Anonymous

Felice di Giardini, 1716-1796

Come, Thou Al-might-y King, Help us Thy Name to sing, Help us to praise: Fa-ther, all glo-ri-ous, O'er all vic-to-ri-ous, Come and reign o-ver us, An-cient of days. A-men.

Come, Thou Incarnate Word,
Gird on Thy mighty sword,
Our prayer attend:
Come, and Thy people bless,
And give Thy word success;
Spirit of holiness,
On us descend.

Come, Holy Comforter,
Thy sacred witness bear
In this glad hour:
Thou who almighty art,
Now rule in every heart,
And ne'er from us depart,
Spirit of power.

To the great One in Three
The highest praises be,
Hence ever more!
His sovereign majesty
May we in glory see,
And to eternity
Love and adore.

Come, Thou Almighty King

The words of this hymn are generally regarded as anonymous, and perhaps this fact adds distinction to its quality and emphasizes its universal character. No man may claim it and we would not know the pen to which its riches should be ascribed. Its earliest form is in five stanzas of seven lines with the title, "An Hymn to the Trinity." It appeared on a tract of four pages, together with stanzas 1, 2, 6, 10, 11 and 12 of Charles Wesley's hymn, "The Backslider," beginning "Jesus, let thy pitying eye." Julian's *Dictionary of Hymnology* states that the date of this tract is unknown, but it is bound with the British Museum copy of the sixth edition of George Whitefield's *Collection* (1757) and again with copies in the same library of the eighth edition, 1759, and the ninth, 1760. It comes to modern hymnals through the appendix to Madden's *Collection* of 1763. If there was a title page to the tract, it was lost, so that any hope of discovering the name of the author is gone. There are many who claim "Come, Thou Almighty King" for Charles Wesley, but his authorship is nothing more than conjecture, even though the great Sedgwick always maintained that Charles Wesley wrote the song.

No hymn has been written into more languages, sung by more peoples, and is more generally claimed and loved by Christians of all communions.

The universal character of the great poem is enhanced by the fact that it was written to be sung to the familiar tune of "God Save the King" and "My Country, 'Tis of Thee." Even the words may have been composed in imitation of the British national anthem. From the volume *Hymns and Hymn Writers of the Church,* we learn that the first two stanzas of the national anthem of England appeared in a publication, *Harmonia Anglicana,* which was issued in 1743 or 1744. These verses were also in existence in Latin at that time and were used in a concert given by the organist of the Chapel Royal on September 28, 1743. "God Save the King," as it is now known, was sung in Drury Lane Theater, London, in honor of King George, and a few days later at Covent Garden. It was received with tumultuous applause. In the next month the words and music were published in the *Gentleman's Magazine* with the third stanza added. It was universally acclaimed and, because of its widespread popularity rather than by any official action, was quickly recognized as the national hymn of England. All of this suggests to some that the author of "Come, Thou Almighty King," since he wrote in this same period, would wish to remain unknown. The words themselves are regarded as an unmistakable imitation of the popular song of the day.

"Come, Thou Almighty King" is adoration of the Trinity with recognition of the Word, and with acknowledgement in eternal praises of their eternal unity. Whether or not Charles Wesley wrote the poem, it is true to his profound conviction and resonant with the music of his radiant faith. No national anthem, no song of any earthly sovereign, has yet approached the majestic richness of this anthem of Christian worship.

The tune to which the hymn is now generally sung is known as "The Italian Hymn," a composition by Felice di Giardini, a famous Italian musician, violinist and composer.

Christ, the Lord, Is Risen Today

Charles Wesley, 1707-1788, and others

From Lyra Davidica, 1708

Christ the Lord is risen to-day, Alleluia! Sons of men and angels say, Alleluia! Raise your joys and triumphs high, Alleluia! Sing, ye heav'ns, and earth reply,— Alleluia! A-men.

Lives again our glorious King, Alleluia!
Where, O death, is now thy sting? Alleluia!
Once He died, our souls to save, Alleluia!
Where's thy victory, boasting grave? Alleluia!

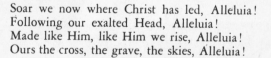

Love's redeeming work is done, Alleluia!
Fought the fight, the battle won, Alleluia!
Death in vain forbids Him rise, Alleluia!
Christ hath opened Paradise, Alleluia!

Soar we now where Christ has led, Alleluia!
Following our exalted Head, Alleluia!
Made like Him, like Him we rise, Alleluia!
Ours the cross, the grave, the skies, Alleluia!

Christ, the Lord, Is Risen Today

It has been written that "among uninspired men whom God has raised up to furnish song for Zion, Watts and Wesley stand preëminent." Not all of us would agree that Watts and Wesley were uninspired; at any rate, our interest in them does not join at the point of theology or dogma. Nor does it concern us which of the two is generally regarded as the greater. Of Watts it is said he "created a people's hymnal," and of Wesley, "a people of hymn singers." Watts enjoyed leisure and did his work after retirement. Wesley moved through constant religious upheaval; his inspirations came from trial and persecution, but his was the triumphant note of world-wide religious revival.

Charles Wesley was born December 18, 1708. He was the third son of the rector of the Episcopal Church at Epworth, England. He began to write hymns when he was twenty-nine and he was still writing in his eightieth year. At the very hour of death, when he could no longer hold a pen, but could not remain silent, he dictated his last hymn. A distinguished son of the Church of England has written, "The Church of England closed her doors against Wesley while living, but now her most magnificent cathedrals echo with such of his hymns as 'Hark, the Herald Angels Sing,' 'Christ, the Lord, Is Risen Today,' and 'Hail the Day that Sees Him Rise.' " Wesley died in 1788.

While there are many Easter songs and while they increase in number if not in quality from year to year, this hymn is one of the recognized and eternal great. A fourteenth-century Easter hymn is the music most frequently used and to this Wesley's Methodists added the "alleluias." Early Christians greeted each other on Easter morning with "Alleluia, the Lord is risen. He is risen indeed." And fitting it is that Charles Wesley's "Christ, the Lord, Is Risen Today," should have become an Easter greeting and song of the Church Universal.

There has grown up throughout America a worthy custom of holding community Easter sunrise services. The first of these was established on a mountain overlooking Riverside, California, where a great cross crowns the summit. Here, toward sunrise, the people gather on the morning of the risen Christ. Slowly, from the valleys below, they come to the appointed place, and out upon the still air, as though lifted on the fingers of the rosy-tinted dawn, the music of this hymn is carried afar. Also, above the mighty chasm of Arizona's Grand Canyon, among the pines of the southern rim, it is sung by the waiting multitude. In stadiums, on hillsides, by the lakes of the north, and in the valleys of the south, it becomes the bugle of the Christian's eternal hope. The heart-warming experience of John Wesley is no less the experience of his brother, and in their united ministry the whole world is blest.

Battle Hymn of the Republic

Written during the War Between the States, this hymn was one of the most dramatic "events" of that momentous period. The author, Julia Ward Howe, had gone with her husband, her pastor and Governor Andrews of Massachusetts for a visit to the nation's capital. She was already established as a popular writer, and with her husband she had been identified with the struggle of the Greeks to achieve freedom. On the occasion of her visit to Washington, the city was crowded with Federal troops. During a military review at some distance from the capital, a threatening move of the enemy brought the maneuvers to an abrupt end. Returning to the city, Julia Ward Howe and her companions heard Union troops singing "John Brown's body lies amouldering in the grave." Dr. Clarke, her pastor, said, "Why do you not write some good words for that stirring tune?" Then came the inspiration and that night the great hymn was born. It appeared in the *Atlantic Monthly* in February, 1862, and immediately attracted wide attention, but its great popularity came as the result of its use by Chaplain C. C. McCabe of the 122nd Ohio Volunteer Infantry.

One of the most dramatic stories associated with "The Battle Hymn of the Republic" is that of Chaplain McCabe, afterwards Bishop McCabe of the Methodist Episcopal Church, who, captured by the Confederates on June 16, 1863, was sent to Libby Prison. Chaplain McCabe had a baritone voice of unusual quality and distinction. Afterward he was to use his voice not only in singing and sermon, but in delivering throughout America one of the most famous lectures of the Civil War and after-war period. Shortly after his imprisonment, word came that the Union forces had suffered an overwhelming defeat; however, a little later, a Negro who brought food to the prisoners whispered the word of victory instead of defeat, that a great battle had been won by the Federal troops. In a moment the prisoners were on their feet cheering wildly. Then the chaplain was called upon to sing, and the words, "Mine eyes have seen the glory of the coming of the Lord," and "Glory, glory, hallelujah," swept over the encampment. It was Libby Prison's celebration of the victory at Gettysburg.

Following the chaplain's release, at a meeting of the Christian Commission in Washington, which was attended by Abraham Lincoln, Chaplain McCabe was asked to describe his experiences, and when the audience called for the song, he gave them "The Battle Hymn of the Republic," verse after verse. The excitement increased, and when he had finished there was tumultuous applause. Abraham Lincoln, with tears streaming over his cheeks, cried, "Sing it again!" and again it was sung. And thus it became a national hymn.

As a very young man, representing a student organization, I was once scheduled to address the students of Ohio Wesleyan University. To the surprise of everyone, Bishop McCabe appeared. He was Wesleyan's most popular personality. The young man was overwhelmed with confusion, but went at once to ask the distinguished visitor to address the chapel audience. It was for this that they turned out. But the bishop declined. Then he said, "Let me pray!" And what a prayer it was! Upon that prayer the young man was raised to accept his opportunity and in it he was presented to the students with such generous understanding that they understood.

Julia Ward Howe was born on May 27, 1819 in Bowling Green, lower New York. She remained active and vital as a writer until her death in 1910, at the age of ninety-one.

Battle Hymn of the Republic

Julia Ward Howe, 1819-1910

"John Brown's Body"

Mine eyes have seen the glory of the coming of the Lord; He is
trampling out the vintage where the grapes of wrath are stored; He hath
loosed the fateful lightning of His terrible swift sword, His truth is marching on.

Chorus

Glory! glory! Halle - lu - jah! Glory! glory! Halle - lu - jah!

Glory! glory! Halle - lu - jah! His truth is marching on.

I have seen Him in the watch-fires of a hundred circling camps;
They have builded Him an altar in the evening dews and damps;
I can read His righteous sentence by the dim of flaring lamps,
His day is marching on.

I have read a fiery gospel, writ in burnish'd rows of steel:
As ye deal with My contemners, so with you My grace shall deal,
Let the Hero, born of woman, crush the serpent with His heel,
Since God is marching on.

He has sounded forth the trumpet that shall never call retreat;
He is sifting out the hearts of men before His judgment seat;
Oh, be swift, my soul, to answer Him! be jubilant, my feet!
Our God is marching on.

O Come, All Ye Faithful

Ascribed to an unknown hymnist of France and written perhaps early in the eighteenth century, this great hymn was first sung in both England and in France as a benediction during the Christmas period. Now it has become the Christmas benediction song of all Christendom.

In five Korean churches on Christmas Sunday in 1935, I listened to thousands of voices lifting this majestic tune, raising in tones of rapture these inspired words. The Korean Christians crowded the beautiful churches of the Presbyterian Mission at Pyengyang. Seated upon their soft mats, faces uplifted to the altar of their sanctuary, they poured out their souls in this inspired song. Now, "O come, all ye faithful, joyful and triumphant" for me will be always associated with that Christmas.

The song was first published in a collection of hymns by John Francis Wade. It was written in Latin and it is said that more than forty English translations have been made. The one with which we are most familiar is by Canon Frederick Oakeley. It was produced in 1841 for the use of the Margaret Street Chapel, London, where Oakeley was the clergyman. It is interesting to note that the English version was never published by the translator, but that it came to public attention as it was sung in his chapel. He was born September 5, 1802, in Shrewsbury, England, and educated at Christ Church, Oxford. After taking holy orders, he was a prebendary of Lichfield Cathedral, then preacher at Whitehall and later a minister of Margaret Chapel, Margaret Street, London, in 1839. In 1845 he resigned his appointments in the Church of England and was received into the Roman communion. Subsequently he became a canon of the cathedral in the Roman Catholic ecclesiastical district of Westminster. He died January 29, 1880. He is best remembered by, and his greatest distinction comes from, this translation of "Adeste Fideles."

It is thought that the hymn and tune came into use together and that they were first used by Roman Catholics in the early eighteenth century. At one time ascribed to St. Bonaventure, it is to be found in no edition of his works. It is believed to be of French or German authorship. "The text appears in three forms, the first is in eight stanzas. . . . As early as 1797 it was sung at the Chapel of the Portuguese Embassy, London, of which Vincent Novello was organist, and the tune, which was ascribed by Novello to John Reading, organist of Westminster Cathedral, 1665-1681, at once became popular." (Julian's *Dictionary of Hymnology.*)

O Come, All Ye Faithful

Tr. by Frederick Oakeley, 1802-1880 and others

Cantus Diversi

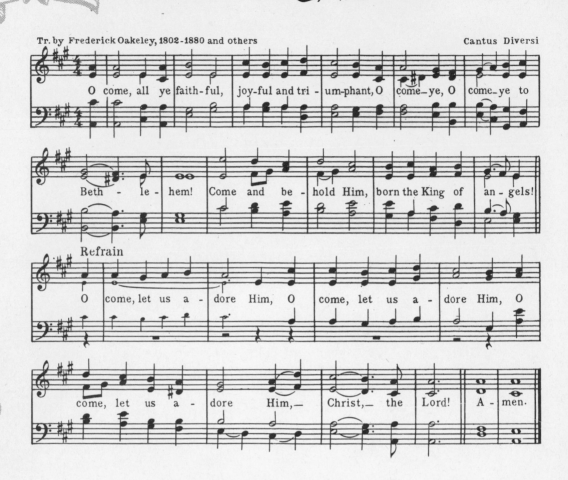

O come, all ye faith-ful, joy-ful and tri-um-phant, O come ye, O come ye to Beth-le-hem! Come and be-hold Him, born the King of an-gels!

Refrain

O come, let us a-dore Him, O come, let us a-dore Him, O come, let us a-dore Him,— Christ,— the Lord! A-men.

Sing, choirs of angels, sing in exultation,
O sing, all ye citizens of heav'n above!
Glory to God, all glory in the highest!

Yea, Lord, we greet Thee, born this happy morning,
Jesus, to Thee be all glory giv'n;
Word of the Father, now in flesh appearing!

A Mighty Fortress Is Our God

Martin Luther, 1483-1546
Tr. by Frederick H. Hedge, 1805-1890

Martin Luther

A might-y for-tress is our God, A bul-wark nev-er fail-ing; Our
help-er He, a-mid the flood Of mor-tal ills pre-vail-ing: For
still our an-cient foe Doth seek to work us woe; His craft and power are great, And,
armed with cru-el hate, On earth is not his qual. A-men.

Did we in our own strength confide,
Our striving would be losing;
Were not the right Man on our side,
The Man of God's own choosing:
Dost ask who that may be?
Christ Jesus, it is He;
Lord Sabaoth, His name,
From age to age the same,
And He must win the battle.

And though this world, with devils filled,
Should threaten to undo us,
We will not fear, for God hath willed
His truth to triumph through us:
The Prince of Darkness grim—
We tremble not for him;
His rage we can endure,
For lo, his doom is sure,
One little word shall fell him.

That word above all earthly powers,
No thanks to them, abideth;
The Spirit and the gifts are ours
Through Him who with us sideth:
Let goods and kindred go,
This mortal life also;
The body they may kill:
God's truth abideth still,
His kingdom is forever.

A Mighty Fortress Is Our God

In July, 1926, in the famous Crystal Palace of London, England, reduced to ruins by a great fire ten years later, "A Mighty Fortress Is Our God" was sung in the first international gathering attended by a German delegation following the World War of 1914-1918. It was a never-to-be-forgotten occasion. Seated on the platform were the most distinguished religious leaders, statesmen, and publicists of their generation. David Lloyd George, Stanley Baldwin, and Ramsay MacDonald were present that night and the latter delivered a notable address.

For many, the atmosphere had been strained and uncertain in the earlier moments of the session, but when the strains of Luther's majestic hymn ("Ein Feste Burg" in the German language) borne upon the tones of the mighty organ, swept over the great audience, the hearts of the people were melted into one. Nearly half a hundred nations were represented in that convention, but the citizenship of all was in the Kingdom of God.

Both the words and tune of this hymn were written by Martin Luther, who was born at Eisleben, Germany, November 10, 1483. He was the son of poor but devout parents. Luther is generally regarded as the father of congregational singing. He wrote his first religious verses after seeing two boys burned at the stake for their profession of the reformed faith.

This tune forms the theme for Meyerbeer's opera "The Huguenots." Also, it has been used by Mendelssohn, Wagner and Bach. It swept across Germany and was famous overnight. It was sung by Luther himself in his hours of greatest danger. Tradition has it that while he lived in Coburg Castle during the time of the Diet of Augsburg and as he translated the Bible into German, he would go to the window and shout this hymn at the top of his voice.

"Ein Feste Burg" had a more distinguished part in the building of the Protestant Church than any other poem or piece of music; it was the very enabling act for the Reformation.

Luther's early life was spent in poverty. Necessity, physical necessity, sent him from door to door singing carols to earn food and shelter. He was a lover of nature, and the song of the birds, the folklore of his people, and the beauty of flowers were the companions of his spirit. Later a woman of means became interested in him and made it possible for him to graduate from the University of Erfurt in 1501. He became an Augustinian monk in 1505 and a priest in 1507.

The forty-sixth Psalm is the foundation of "Ein Feste Burg," which, in the opinion of some, accomplished as much for the Reformation as did the translation of the Bible. Sung at Luther's funeral, its first line is carved upon his tomb.

In recent times the great hymn came again into its own. Throughout the German-occupied countries of Europe the spiritual descendants of Martin Luther have stood before their closed churches and in the snows of Norway or upon the dykes of Holland, in the agony of twentieth-century martyrdom, singing "A Mighty Fortress Is Our God."

Contents